PROTOTYPE LOCOMOTIVES

ROBERT TUFNELL

DAVID & CHARLES

NEWTON ABBOT LONDON NORTH POMFRET (Vt)

British Library Cataloguing in Publication Data

Tufnell, R. M.
Prototype locomotives.—(Locomotive studies)
1. Locomotives—Great Britain—History
I. Title II. Series
625.2'6'0941 TJ603.4.G7

ISBN 0–7153–8397–3

Photoset in Times
by Northern Phototypesetting Co., Bolton
and printed in Great Britain
by Biddles Ltd., Guildford, Surrey
for David & Charles (Publishers) Limited
Brunel House Newton Abbot Devon

Published in the United States of America
by David & Charles Inc
North Pomfret Vermont 05053 USA

CONTENTS

ACKNOWLEDGEMENTS

The Author would like to thank the following sources of information:-

Messrs T. Mathewson-Dick, T. C. B. Miller, MBE, A. J. Sykes and A. T. H. Taylor

Book Sources

Nock, O. S. *Stars Castles & Kings* (David & Charles 1980)
Brown, F. A. S. *Nigel Gresley* (Ian Allan)
Webb, B. *English Electric Main Line Diesel Locomotives of British Rail* (David & Charles 1976)

Technical Papers

The Institution of Locomotive Engineers *Proceedings*, 1946 Journal No 191, 1950 Journal No 214, 1952 Journal No 227, 1958 Journal No 266, 1962 Journals Nos 286 and 287.
The Institution of Mechanical Engineers *Proceedings* 1910 March p 399
The Institution of Electrical Engineers *Proceedings*, 1948 Volume 95 Part 2, 1950 Volume 97 Part 1a.
The Railway Gazette, November 1945
The Engineer, January & February 1927
The Railway Magazine, March 1931
Diesel Railway Traction, February 1958, May 1960, July 1962, April and November 1963
Railway World, September 1954
British Railways Performance & Efficiency Tests. Bulletins No 1, (May 1951), 9 & 16 (November 1952)
SLS *Journals* April 1969, May and June 1959, January 1970
Society of Automotive Engineers (New York) November 1957
British Railways Rugby Testing Station Report, February 1959
English Electric Mechanical Engineering Laboratory Report No W/M (lc) p 1283 February, 1967
English Electric Journal March 1966 Volume 21
BRCW/AEI/Sulzer publication *Lion*
Brush Electrical Engineering publication *Falcon*
Vulcan Foundry Magazine 1960, Volume 5 No 4

The London Regional Transport Museum
The London Underground Railway Society
The Narrow Gauge Railway Society
The National Railway Museum
The North Western Museum of Science & Technology
The Public Records Office
The Scottish Record Office
The Swindon Public Library
The University of Sheffield
The City of Glasgow District Council Libraries Department

INTRODUCTION

One of Noel Coward's favourite songs is concerned with the fate of certain unusual characters and was entitled 'I wonder what happened to him'. Similar thoughts may have occurred to students of locomotive design about the fate of some unusual locomotives, descriptions of which have appeared in the technical press or in papers given to engineering institutions, before they disappeared from sight.

This book fills the gaps as far as possible, and assesses the success or failure of such unusual locomotives, the aims of the projects, the technical feasibility of the designs in the light of the contemporary technology, and attempts to see what impact if any, they had on subsequent designs.

Ever since Richard Trevithick made the first steam locomotive run at Penydarren in 1804, designers have been searching in the quest for an improved machine. At first it was just getting the contraption to work at all, but once the basic principles had been established in Stephenson's *Rocket* in 1829, the development of the steam locomotive has followed that for the stationary and marine steam engines, namely greater power output, improved fuel consumption and better reliability.

These same three criteria also apply to the diesel and electric successors of the steam unit – in particular the question of power output to the diesel prime mover, and that of reliability to the electric haulage units.

During the nineteenth century there was not much that called for innovation in locomotive design, and though there had been some attempts to follow the marine engine lead and to try out compound designs, these had not proved any more economical overall.

1895 was to prove a turning point because in that year the rival East and West Coast lines from London to Scotland awoke from their lethargy and staged the famous races to Aberdeen, the fastest run on 22 August taking 512 minutes for the 540 miles using the West Coast route. The London &

Armstrong-Whitworth main line 880hp 2–C–2 diesel electric locomotive, built 1933. *W. H. Whitworth/Rail Archive Stephenson*

HS4000 *Kestrel* on the quayside at Harwich, about to be loaded for the USSR. *Brush Electrical Machines Ltd.*

North Western Railway also carried out a non-stop run of 299 miles from Euston to Carlisle. The Great Western Railway had recently completed the conversion from its original 7ft $0\frac{1}{4}$in broad gauge to the 4ft $8\frac{1}{2}$in standard gauge, and under its new chairman Viscount Emlyn had instituted a programme of new lines to South Wales and to the West of England, together with higher speeds.

This does not imply that locomotive design lacked innovation in the era before 1895, and the two most significant attempts at improvement were the use of compounding and the adoption of the piston valve. As mentioned later, compounding was best applied when the piston speeds were comparatively low, and in any case the limitations of loading gauge in this country did not permit the use of adequate sized outside cylinders.

The leading exponents of compounding were Francis Webb of the LNWR at Crewe and Thomas W. Worsdell of the NER at Gateshead. Though both produced some designs of fast passenger locomotives – in particular Webb's Teutonic class which took part in the Race to the North, and Worsdell's J Class of which No 1518 was recorded as producing 1069hp at 86mph – none of these was to have any significant impact on future designs.

The piston valve first used by Worsdell on his D Class compound No 340 was designed by Walter Mackersie Smith and was a success from the start. This feature did have a real significance on future locomotive design and it was Churchward who showed how to get the most out of it.

The next 20 years up to the outbreak of the 1914–18 war saw tremendous developments in locomotive power in four- and six-coupled forms on all the main lines, but none of them approached in such a truly scientific manner as the method adopted by G. J. Churchward on the Great Western. He built a complete range of prototypes, but was the only one to do so in that era.

This was the supreme era of steam locomotive traction and the railway world in general. Until 1904 when 100mph was first attained by a motor vehicle at Ostend, the railway train was the fastest method of travel and every schoolboy wanted to be a train driver. The Great Western Railway also was credited with achieving 100mph in 1904 and, though this has since been a subject of doubt it was possible to regularly travel in trains attaining 60mph, 70mph and even sometimes 80mph.

The Second World War of 1939–45 was followed by a period of re-organisation, culminating in nationalisation and leading first to the dieselisation programme and later to important new main line electrification. Initially the running was made by the railways themselves as a legacy of the 'Big Four' era, the LMS and Southern each producing three main line diesels, and the former Great Western trying out two gas turbines. However none came into revenue-earning service until after nationalisation. After that the running was left to the private contractors as part of their quest for overseas markets, but being at least ten years behind the Americans this was a lost cause.

This review has been divided into four categories, steam, diesel, electric and gas turbine. In the first two categories there were successes and failures; in the electric section they could all be called success ventures, but the gas turbine story is unfortunately a sorry one.

In view of the limitations of space, certain types perhaps worthy of inclusion have had to be left out since they had little influence on locomotive policy in the UK. Included in these are the Holden "Decapod" of 1902 which was primarily an anti-electrification gesture and like so many prototypes was eliminated by overweight and high fuel consumption. The Bulleid "Leader" could be said to fall into this category, but on account of its novel features this is included at the end of the steam era. In the diesel category mention should be made of the first main line diesel-electric locomotive in the UK, the 880hp 2–6–2 (1–C–1) produced by Armstrong-Whitworth in 1933.

The firm of Sir W. G. Armstrong-Whitworth,

having entered the locomotive business in 1919, tried to produce a steam turbine locomotive, but this was rather a disaster. However, that did not dissuade the company from trying out new forms of locomotives propulsion, and in 1926 it launched into the diesel field, first by using engines supplied by Sulzer Bros of Switzerland and later by taking a licence to build the engines at its works at Scotswood-on-Tyne. Following the building of some 1,700hp mobile diesel-electric power units for the Buenos Aires Great Southern Railway (BAGS) in 1932, Armstrong-Whitworth produced an 880hp unit for demonstration and trials on the LNER in the following year.

That version was powered by a Sulzer 8-cylinder 8LD28 engine producing 800hp at 700rpm and driving a Laurence Scott main generator. There were three axle-hung Crompton Parkinson traction motors with control gear, probably by Allen West. The main generator field current was controlled by a hydraulic servo-motor operated by engine oil pressure, which enabled full engine output to be available from 6mph to 65mph. There was also an auxiliary 80hp Armstrong Saurer 6BXD engine and generator which supplied the starting current for the main engine as well as the cooling fan, the compressor and the exhauster. There was apparently no provision for train heating, which limited the locomotive's winter use to freight operation.

Its initial test with 17 coaches (550 tons) on the North Wylam line took place in July 1933 and was witnessed by Nigel Gresley. Following this, it carried out some runs with empty stock to Alnmouth and Hexham. In 1934 it worked freight trains of 45 to 60 wagons between Berwick, Newcastle and York, and its final duty was to work a special train between Leeds and Darlington on 7 June 1934 for delegates of the Institute of Transport Congress.

Shortly after that it suffered a crankcase explosion and was withdrawn having run just over 26,000 miles and consuming 25,200 gallons of fuel. The engine was rebuilt and fitted into a 5ft 6in gauge locomotive which ran for a short time in Ceylon and ultimately found its way to the BAGS system.

Also in the diesel category were the two English Electric 500hp high-speed shunters, which did lead indirectly to the Class 16 diesel-hydraulics, of which No D0226 is still in action on the Worth Valley Railway. There was also the Brush *Hawk* rebuilt from the NBL No 10800, never actually

English Electric Co 500hp No D226, built 1957, on the Worth Valley Railway in 1973. *R. M. Tufnell*

used on rail, and the 4,000hp *Kestrel*, unable to develop its full potential because of overweight, but it is believed still to be running in Russia, and was last reported seen near Bucharest in 1978.

There is still one locomotive running on British Rail that could be called a prototype, namely No 47 901 which acted as a test bed for the latest English Electric (Ruston) engine, the 12RK3CT, producing 3,500hp from 12 cylinders and intended for the Class 58 freight locomotives.

In the electrical section it was necessary to omit the North Eastern Railway freight locomotives and the 1,500v *Tommy* built for the Manchester, Sheffield and Wath scheme.

A summary of the salient features of the prototypes is given in Appendix 1.

Appendix 2 is intended to show the relative overall efficiency from fuel to rail. In the case of the reciprocating steam locomotive this was usually around six percent for a superheated version and much lower for one with saturated steam only. The diesel units show up best with up to 22 percent, but the gas turbine again gives a poor showing. The electric system is of course dependent on the efficiency of the power station supplying the electricity, and for the versions included in the review, the maximum station efficiency at that time was only about 15 percent; the latest overall figure for the CEGB is just over 32 percent.

In overall operation in the UK the diesel loses against the electric locomotive due to higher maintenance costs, but this again is offset by the higher capital charges of the electrification installation and these variants cannot be shown in a table of this nature.

Finally this book is by way of being a tribute to the late Brian Webb with whom the author was co-operating in the production of this review, and whose death will be felt by all those who enjoyed his writings on locomotive matters.

CHAPTER ONE

GREAT WESTERN RAILWAY NO 40

The Great Western Railway was magic to its fans right up to 1939, after which the combined efforts of Hitler and nationalisation for ever tarnished what had been one of Britain's jewels. The Great Western had been fortunate in having a balanced market between its passenger and freight traffic, and of its passenger traffic very little was of the commuter sort which hardly produces the most enthusiastic railway fans. Its passenger traffic was of the business type to Birmingham and to South Wales, but above all it was THE holiday line to the South West. Trains could, and sometimes did, arrive hours late, but that did not matter to the passengers, for they were on holiday.

Part of this magic was due to the West Country welcome one felt on arrival at Paddington – 'Platvarm wun me dear'. But above all to enthusiasts it was due to the Great Western's superb fleet of fast 4–6–0 locomotives, the Saints and Stars, which hauled nearly all its express passenger trains from 1905 until 1923 when the Castles appeared. There were only 77 Saints and 73 Stars built, but what an impact they made. This is the story of the first of the Star class, due to the genius of George Jackson Churchward.

The Great Western Railway had started by being the leading exponent of high-speed operation, using Brunel's broad gauge of 7ft 0¼in, but it had been compelled to abandon this feature in order to conform to the standard 4ft 8½in gauge of the rest of the rail system in England, Wales and Scotland. This conversion involved such a divergence of effort away from the operational side that by the time this exercise was completed in 1892 the GWR's standard of speed and locomotive design had fallen below that of some of its competitors.

In 1895 the new chairman, Viscount Emlyn in conjunction with a new Superintendent of the Line, T. I. Allen, set about reviving the old Great Western spirit. New cut-off lines were proposed to the West of England, to South Wales and to Birmingham. The damaging enforced stop for the refreshment rooms at Swindon was eliminated by their purchase for £100,000. This proved a very good investment since annual profits of around £80,000 were earned initially, although these gradually fell away when the Westbury line was opened. In that year also non-stop runs from London to Bath and Bristol were started from 1 October. The following year (1896) the down Cornishman ran non-stop to Exeter, 194 miles in 225 minutes, using new water troughs at Goring and Keynsham, fed from the Thames and Avon respectively. In the same year Swindon produced its first 4–6–0 locomotive, No 36, with 4ft 8in driving wheels intended for freight traffic, but this was displaced by the 2–6–0 Aberdares following the trials of 2–6–0 No 33 built in 1900.

Between 1894 and 1899 Swindon had produced 80 of the Dean singles, the Achilles class 4–2–2 with 7ft 8in driving wheels, and 161 4–4–0s of various classes using both 5ft 8in and 6ft 8in driving wheels. Just as George Jackson Churchward was taking over from William Dean in 1902, the first 4–6–0 passenger locomotive, No 100 was produced at Swindon.

G. J. Churchward, like many of the former pioneers of steam such as Newcomen, Trevithick, and Hornblower, came from the West Country

Great Western 4-cylinder 4–4–2 No 40 *North Star*, as built.

and he, with typical West Country deliberation proved to be the right man in the right place and at the right time. While awaiting to take over the duties as locomotive superintendent, his appraisal of the motive power requirements of the Great Western caused him to prepare in 1901 a scheme for six standard classes of locomotive:

Class	*Wheel arrangement*	*Driving wheels ft*	*in*	*Outside cylinders (2) in*	*Prototype running number*
1	2-8-0	4	7½	18 x 30	97
2	4-6-0	5	8	18 x 30	–
3	4-6-0	6	8½	18 x 30	98
4	2-6-2T	5	8	18 x 30	99
5	4-4-2T	6	8½	18 x 30	2221
6	4-4-0	6	8½	18 x 30	3473

These were subsequently amended by the omission of Class 2 and the addition of four further classes.

Class	*Wheel arrangement*	*Driving wheels ft*	*in*	*Cylinders No.*	*in*	*Protype running number*
7	4-6-0	6	8½	4	14¼ x 26	40
8	4-6-2	6	8½	4	14¼ x 26	111
9	2-6-0	5	8	2	18 x 30	4301
10	2-8-0T	4	8	2	18½ x 30	4201

In August 1902 there had arrived in the Swindon drawing office a drawing of a boiler used on the Illinois Central Railroad, showing a tapered rear half to the barrel carrying a steam dome and a tapered firebox. This boiler had a grate area of 27.2sq ft, a barrel 13ft 0in long and a working pressure of 210 lb/sq in. This seems to have led to the evolution of six standard boilers in 1903 as shown in the diagram bottom left, the technical details of which are shown in Table 1.

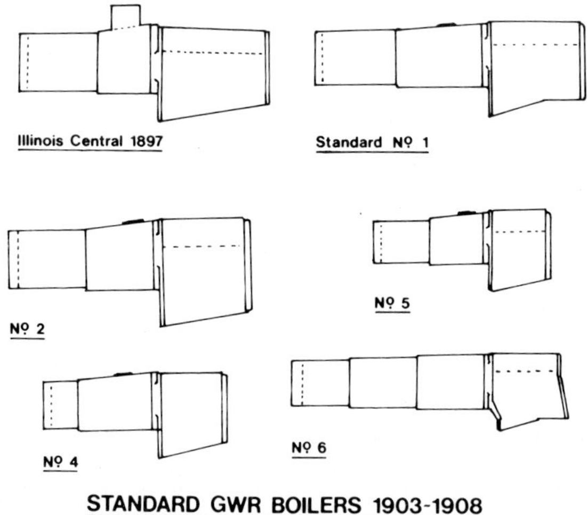

STANDARD GWR BOILERS 1903-1908

The major difference between the Illinois Central and the Swindon boilers was the elimination of the steam dome in the Swindon design, as this was considered a point of weakness. Great attention was paid to the shape of the firebox side plates so as to ensure the maximum flow of water to the hottest part of the system.

Having four types of firebox to choose from, the Belpaire type originally adopted by Alfred Belpaire of the Belgian State Railroad in 1861 was selected as this could be accomodated between the rear driving wheels, and provided the greatest steam volume. The round top was the most favoured in the UK at that time as being the cheapest to produce, but it brought some problems with the varying lengths of stays. The Wooten type introduced by John E. Wooten for the Philadelphia & Reading Railroad in 1866 was the most suitable for low calorific value fuels, but entailed a non-driving trailing axle in order to house the extra width. A combined Belpaire-Wooten type was selected by Churchward for use in the Standard No 6 boiler used only in the Pacific No 111 *The Great Bear*.

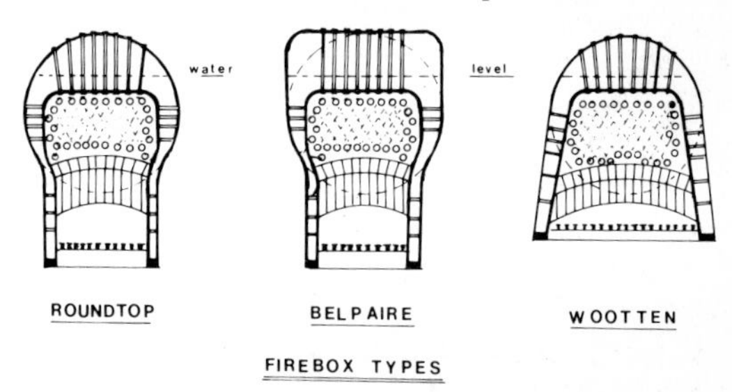

FIREBOX TYPES

Churchward boilers were reputed to have been expensive, but this is rather a relative term in view of their longevity and good performance. The costs at the date of manufacture is not known, but book values quoted in 1913 were:

Standard No 1 £433, Standard No 2 £285, Standard No 3 £322, Standard No 4 £310, Standard No 5 £330.

Two other features of the Swindon standard boilers which must be mentioned are superheating and the top feed arrangement, introduced in 1906 and 1911 respectively. These will be dealt with in the development story of No 40.

Having established the standard boiler and locomotive types, the first of the prototypes were built in 1903 – No 98 in March, No 97 in June, and

No 99 in September. Meantime, reports had come to Swindon of the excellent results being obtained by some de Glehn compound Atlantics in use on the Nord line in France, so to ensure that this aspect was not overlooked one was ordered from the Société Alsacienne des Constructions Méchaniques at Belfort. This locomotive, which arrived at Swindon in October 1903, had a boiler pressure of 227 lb/sq in. To provide a true comparison, the successor to No 98 – No 171 (later No 2971) – was rebuilt as a 4–4–2, and its boiler pressure raised to 225 lb/sq in. At the same time it was named *Albion*.

Most steam engines in use at that time for land and marine applications made use of the compound system, some of the larger marine engines being quadruple expansion with outputs up to 20,000hp. Although attempts had been made by the North Eastern Railway and the London & North Western Railway to apply compounding to rail traction, these had not been a great success. More successful applications had been made on the Continent starting with Von Borries in Germany in 1897, and compound locomotives were operating successfully in Germany, Austria and in France.

In general compounding seems to have been more successful when applied to freight operation, and George Hughes of the Lancashire & Yorkshire Railway in a paper entitled 'Compounding and Superheating' given to the Institution of Mechanical Engineers in March 1910, came to the conclusion that compounding was best applied when the piston speed was not above 600ft/minute. His most successful applications of compounding were on the L&YR 0–8–0 freight locomotives where the piston speeds were around 700ft/minute at 30mph. Similarly, Webb's only effective use of compounding on the LNWR was on the 0–8–0 freight type, of which 170 were built and which had a piston speed of under 500ft/min at 30mph.

The tractive effort of de Glehn compound No 102 was 23,710 lb, and that of Swindon's No 171 was 23,090 lb. Comparative trials between these two, as well as the slightly larger de Glehn compounds Nos 103 and 104 which were delivered in June 1905 – their tractive effort was 27,000lb – did not show any marked benefit for the compound system under GWR operating conditions.

This could have been due to two reasons – first, the de Glehn design did not have the generous valve openings of the Swindon build, and, second, the driving of a compound demands much greater discipline and training which European drivers accepted as against the rather individualistic British approach. A typical British driver's description of himself was 'self-taught and underpaid'.

By the end of 1905, Swindon had produced a further nineteen 2-cylinder locomotives of the No 171 type, six as 4–6–0s, and thirteen as 4–4–2s:

Original No.	*Wheel arrangement*	*Later No*	*Name*
172	4–4–2	2972	*The Abbot*
173	4–6–0	2973	*Robins Bolitho*
174	4–6–0	2974	*Lord Barrymore*
175	4–6–0	2975	*Viscount Churchill*
176	4–6–0	2976	*Winterstoke*
177	4–6–0	2977	*Robertson*
178	4–6–0	2978	*Kirkland*
179	4–4–2	2979	*Quentin Durward*
180	4–4–2	2980	*Coeur de Lion*
181	4–4–2	2981	*Ivanhoe*
182	4–4–2	2982	*Lalla Rookh*
183	4–4–2	2983	*Redgauntlet*
184	4–4–2	2984	*Guy Mannering*
185	4–4–2	2985	*Peveril of the Peak*
186	4–4–2	2986	*Robin Hood*
187	4–4–2	2987	*Bride of Lammermoor*
188	4–4–2	2988	*Rob Roy*
189	4–4–2	2989	*Talisman*
190	4–4–2	2990	*Waverley*

From correspondents' reports of runs on the Great Western in 1905 the de Glehns seem to have kept good times to Plymouth with 197ton trains averaging 55mph to 56mph, but the better runs seem to have been achieved by the GWR locomotives. No 98 averaged 61mph to Bristol with 410 tons; No 173 ran to Swindon at 60mph with 472 tons, and No 183 came from Exeter to Paddington with 300 tons at 59mph. During three winter months, out of 83 runs from Bristol to London, 58 were at over 60mph with the best at 64.1mph.

As a result of these tests the 4–6–0 had shown itself superior for operation on the arduous hill sections between Newton Abbot and Plymouth, but the 4-cylinder compounds had shown much better running characteristics at speed, and thus was born the 4-cylinder simple expansion 4–6–0 No 40, produced in 1906. Before finalising the design, No 40 was built as a 4–4–2 and tested in that form, but the next ten locomotives, Nos 4001

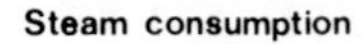

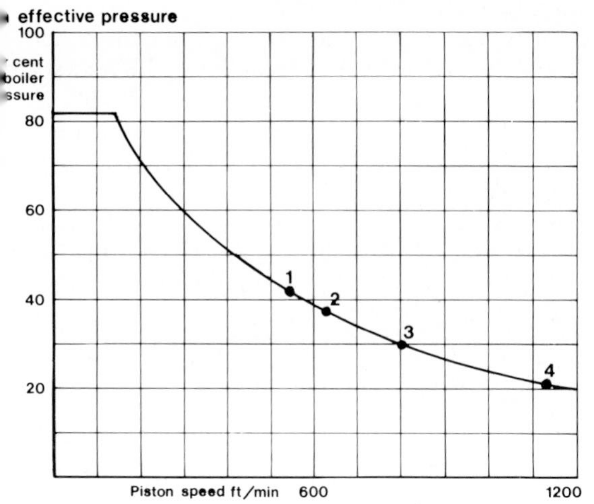

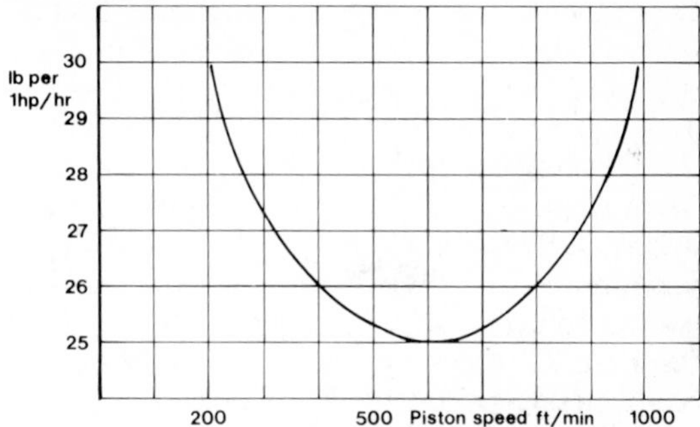

1 STAR at 60 mph
2 SAINT at 60 mph
3 DUCHESS at 80 mph
4 A4 at 126 mph

L&YR DYNAMOMETER CAR TEST RESULTS

to 4010, were all produced as 4–6–0s, bearing 'Star' names.

By 1906 considerable transformation, initiated in 1895, had taken place on the GWR. In 1903 the direct line to South Wales between Wootton Bassett and Patchway had cut ten miles off that route, non-stop runs to Plymouth (246 miles via Bristol) had been initiated in 1904, and in 1906 the completion of the line between Castle Cary and Cogload Junction had cut 21 miles off the run from London to the West Country.

The 100-mile stretch of line between Reading and Cogload Junction could be called the longest railway bypass in the UK, nearly double that of the Trent Valley line between Rugby and Stafford which cut out Birmingham; that only saved seven miles, but also gave rise to the song 'Oh, Mr Porter'. No songs celebrated the cutting-out of Bath and Bristol, and the line through Westbury was certainly not up to Brunel's standard, being wandering and hilly; even now parts of the Reading–Cogload line are limited to 90mph or less. Water troughs had been installed at Aldermaston, Westbury and Creech – those at Westbury had cost just over £11,000.

Churchward had obtained approval for his 4-cylinder express locomotives on the basis of an estimated cost of £3,600, but like many railway estimates of costs for locomotives built in the Great Western Railway works, this seems to have been rather optimistic. The French-built de Glehns had cost £3,200 for No 102 *La France* and £4,107 for the larger No 103 *President* and No 104 *Alliance*. These prices were without tenders, and the standard GWR 6-wheel tender was then around £450.

The Swindon 2-cylinder Atlantic No 171 was quoted as £2,632, but again book figures for these in 1913 are given as £4,600 for the 2-cylinder 4–6–0s and £4,862 for the 4-cylinder version. This seems to bear out the argument by the private locomotive builders that there was no true comparison in building costs between theirs and those built in railway shops.

Some comparable figures for other contemporary locomotives are £3,950 for a 1905 Atlantic for the LBSCR, £2,937 for an Atlantic for the GNR, and £4,260 for a 4–6–0 by Beyer Peacock for the GCR in 1906.

No 40 as first produced had a tractive effort of 25,090 lb with a cylinder diameter of 14¼in, but in 1909 when it was converted to a 4–6–0 and named *North Star*, the cylinder diameter was increased to 15in and the tractive effort to 27,800lb. This latter figure was the same as that obtained by No 111, the first Pacific to be produced in the UK, which came out in 1908.

The 4–6–2 Pacific type had first been introduced into regular service by the Missouri-Pacific Railroad in 1902, and into Europe in 1907 when No. 4501 was produced by the Société Alsacienne for the Paris–Orleans section of the French system, and while a success in those applications, was not really justified on the Great Western. The length and weight of No 111 led to severe route limitations, and it was no more powerful than the 4–6–0 Star class using the same cylinders and boiler pressure. Due to its boiler length it was a poor steamer, but if it had proved operationally superior to the Stars, the necessary civil work would have been put in hand for a more widespread use.

GWR No 40 *North Star*, rebuilt as a 4–6–0. *BR/OPC*

No 40 differed from the other Stars in that the valve operating mechanism was not driven by an eccentric, but used one inside crosshead to provide this effect for the other inside cylinder. The outside valves were worked by rocking levers from their own inside valve gears. This so-called Scissors valve gear worked satisfactorily on No 40 until it was rebuilt as a Castle in 1929, but the arrangement was not used on the other Stars as there was a risk that a breakage would put the locomotive completely out of service, whereas with the Walschaert gear used on the rest of the class the locomotives could get home on two cylinders in emergency.

Having developed the steam-producing unit to the desired result, attention was paid to the other components concerned with getting the steam to and from the cylinders. Starting with the regulator valve of the jockey valve type, this was designed following considerable detail development to ensure the control of steam admission as shown in the diagram right, which was largely instrumental in obviating wheelslip on starting heavy loads.

Next, the valve gear was intended to give the maximum flow of steam, and the principles adopted for the 2-cylinder engines Nos 98 and 171 were followed. The piston valves on the Saints were of 10in bore by $5\frac{7}{8}$in travel; those for No 40 were of 8in bore by 7in travel. Apart from the Scissors gear on No 40, the other 4-cylinder locomotives used an inside Walschaert gear with the outside valves operated by rocker arms from the inside cylinders, thus keeping the usual clean external Great Western appearance.

Finally, the smokebox and blastpipe arrangement, which underwent considerable testing on the stationary plant at Swindon, was the one feature where more attention could have been paid to the layout particularly in regard to the pipework from the external cylinders. This feature was improved on the later Castles, and these gave better specific fuel consumption. From 1929 some of the Stars were fitted with external pipes from the outside cylinders, no doubt with beneficial results.

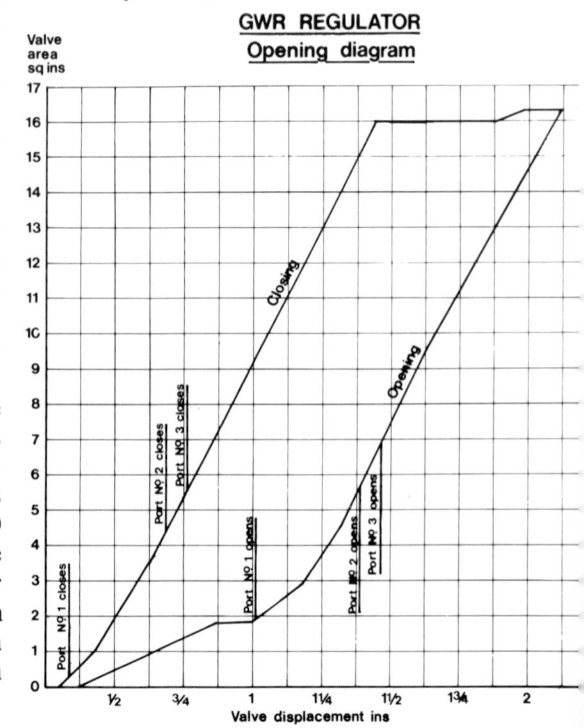

One point of weakness in No 40 as produced had been the connecting rods which were fluted and which showed a tendency to bend, but these were later increased in thickness and the problem overcome.

Just after No 40 was produced, experimental work was started in the use of superheaters at Swindon in 1906. Superheaters had first been used in 1850 by Hirn and Alsace; this had been limited to 100°C because of the use of organic oils, but with the developing use of mineral oil the temperature was raised by Schmidt of Kassel to 350°C. In 1897 Henschel had fitted a superheater to a 4–4–0 of the Hanover State Railway and one had been tried by the L&Y in 1899 on one of its Aspinall Atlantics.

The application of superheating on the Great Western had originally only been intended to prevent cylinder condensation and the true value of superheating was not then appreciated, since no data of steam properties above saturation point were available until Professor Callender of Glasgow produced his tables in 1913. These show (for instance) that an increase in boiler pressure from 200 lb/sq in to 225 lb/sq in in saturated steam increased the total heat in calories per lb from 670.45 to 671.64, whereas by superheating by only 100°C this could be increased to 727 calories.

Since the efficiency of a steam engine can only be improved either by increasing the initial total heat or reducing the heat of emission on the basis of the Rankine formula $\frac{H1-H2}{H1}$, assuming the same back pressure, an increase in steam temperature at 200 lb/sq in by superheating by 100°C would increase the theoretical Rankine efficiency from 4.7 per cent to 11.8 per cent. This would justify the fuel savings and improved performance obtained by the application of even a low grade of superheat to the Star class fleet. This was borne out by the results, as according to figures quoted by Churchward, 625 locomotives had been fitted with superheaters by 1913 at a cost of £90 per unit and this had saved 60,000 tons of coal. As the GWR was paying around 12s 0d [60p] per ton at that time this saving would show a return of 64 per cent if the figures are to be trusted.

Swindon's approach to the application of superheating was typical, with the fitting first of a Schmidt superheater to No 2901 *Lady Superior* in 1906, followed by a Cole type to No 4010 *Western Star* in 1907, but these were found to be difficult to maintain in that they could not be removed intact through the smokebox door.

Three types of Swindon-designed superheaters were then built and fitted to Nos 4011, 2922, and 2913 respectively; the last one fitted in 1909 to *Saint Andrew* became the standard for the No 1 boiler. This had two rows of seven units of 1in tubes with 248sq ft of heating surface. According to test results published by British Rail in 1950 after comprehensive tests on a Hall class fitted with a standard No 1 boiler, the admission steam temperatures varied from 500°F at 8,000lb of steam per hour, to 600°F at 26,000lb per hour, a maximum superheat of 200°F (111°C).

One of the problems at the time, when superheating was introduced was that of lubrication. Churchward's comment during the discussion on Hughes' paper in 1910 was to stress the importance of lubrication to the cylinders even when steam was shut-off. At that time lubrication was usually only fed into the steam for atomisation, because of the dangers of excessive oil getting back to the boiler and causing priming. The Swindon superheated boilers were provided with a special valve operated by the steam regulator so as to pass oil to the cylinders under all conditions.

One other feature that was adopted for all the Swindon boilers from 1911 was that of top feed for the water, to valves within the safety-valve casing on the top of the boiler. The water then was fed onto trays leading forward so as to mix the water at the front of the boiler barrel. This resulted in most of the hard deposits settling in the trays which could be cleaned by removing the safety-valve casing This proved as successful as the water softening adopted by other railway systems, and resulted in boiler life of over 400,000 miles before renewal.

No 40 did not have all these refinements until 1913, by which time it had 15in bore cylinders, a full taper boiler with the No 3 superheater, top feed trays, a de Glehn type bogie and its final number, 4000.

By that time the last of the short cuts planned in 1895 had been opened, that from Princess Risborough to Aynho, providing a direct route to Birmingham, cutting out the Oxford loop and saving almost ten miles, thus enabling a two-hour run to Birmingham. This finally removed the stigma of the 'Great Way Round' formerly applied to the GWR. These lines are shown in the accompanying map.

Swindon had installed its own locomotive

Great Western Railway No 40

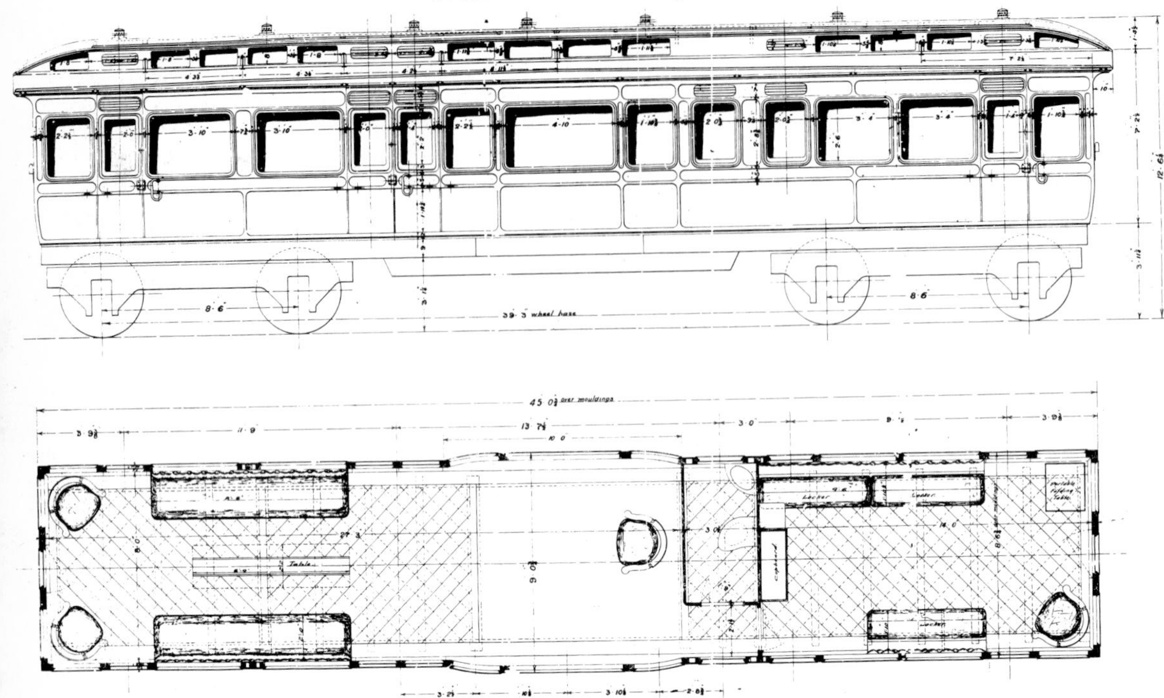

The Great Western Railway dynomometer car.

testing plant in 1903 and had built a dynamometer car at a cost of £1,076. This dynamometer car was at one time loaned to the North Eastern Railway which built a duplicate of it, which became the LNER car that recorded the 126mph achieved by LNER Class A4 4–6–2 No 4468 *Mallard* on 3 July 1938. Considerable testing was carried out on the Swindon stationary plant in order to establish the best design of smokebox and blastpipes, but there does not seem to have been much true performance testing, possibly because the plant in its original form could only absorb around 500hp.

Later when it was learned that the Rugby test plant was being considered, the Swindon plant was quietly rebuilt to absorb the full output of locomotives then in production. Dynamometer car tests must have been carried out, but it was said that Churchward was not very interested in these and the results seem to have been lost, but there is one record of a trial with Star No 4013 on 28 April 1908 with a 368ton train from Plymouth to Paddington. This was using saturated steam, and established Churchward's desired result to obtain a drawbar pull of two tons at 70mph.

One recorded run by No 40 from Paddington to Plymouth started with 290 tons to Westbury, and after dropping the slip portions there and at Taunton and Exeter, finished with 185 tons. The times were 92 minutes to Westbury, 142 minutes to Taunton and 170 minutes to Exeter. Uphill speeds were 43mph at Whiteball, 24mph at Dainton and 25mph at Rattery. It was noted that adhesion was barely adequate so presumably the locomotive was in the 4–4–2 form. This hardly compares to one run recorded with No 2922 *Saint Gabriel* – when setting out from Paddington 15 minutes late with 530 tons it arrived at Plymouth on time!

The fitting of superheaters increased the drawbar pull at 70mph to almost three tons, but more importantly it enabled larger trains to be worked non-stop to Plymouth. The standard GWR tender only held six tons of coal, so that for a run of 225 miles the consumption could not exceed 59 lb/mile, and for the saturated locomotives the load was limited to 200 tons. When the 10.30 am Limited was introduced the use of superheated locomotives allowed this to be increased to over 500 tons as far as Westbury. In general the operation of the Stars was excellent and they carried the brunt of the Great Western high-speed main line workings until the arrival of the Castle class in 1923.

No 4000 was finally withdrawn from service in May 1957. Since the Stars averaged around

40,000 miles a year, and allowing for repairs and rebuild, the locomotive probably ran well over two million miles.

By 1911 the Great Western was in a very sound financial position; the annual receipts of £14 million were made up of £7.2 million from freight and £6.8 million from passengers. The net operating profit was £5.4 million and an ordinary dividend of over 5 percent had been paid consistently since 1901. Passenger train miles had increased from 27 million in 1903 to 33 million in 1911, but the coal cost had also gone up from £610,000 to £750,000, largely due to heavier train weights per passenger owing to corridor stock, dining cars and increased comfort generally.

The steam locomotive was the dominant piece of engineering in most peoples' lives at that time, particularly as regards speed, and the Great Western Stars were the supreme example – the doyen of schoolboys of all ages up to at least 60.

Table 1
Swindon Standard Boilers, 1903–1908

Boiler Std No.	*Barrel length ft in*	*Firebox length ft in*	*Grate area sq ft*	*Heating surface sq ft*	*Pressure lb/sq in*	*Taper*	*Used on*	
							prototypes	*classes*
1	14 10	9 0	27.1	2,142	225	Full	40, 96, 98, 171	28xx 29xx 40xx 49xx 68xx
2	11 2	7 0	20.3	1,349	200	$\frac{1}{2}$	99 2221 3373	31xx 22xx 4120 33xx
3	10 3	7 0	213	1,550	200	$\frac{1}{2}$		36xx
4	11 0	7 0	20.6	1,818	200	$\frac{3}{4}$	3473 33 3405	38xx 43xx 37xx 42xx
5	10 6	5 0	16.6	1,273	200	$\frac{1}{2}$		45xx
6	23 0	8 0	41.8	3,403	225	Full	111	

Table 2
Steps in the Development of No 40

Year	*Loco No*	*Wheel arrangement*	*Driving wheel diameter ft in*	*Boiler pressure lb/sq in*	*No*	*Cylinders Dia.*	*Stroke*	*Tractive effort lb*	*Boiler*
1896	36	4–6–0	4 8	180	2	20in	24in		Parallel
1899	2601	4–6–0	4 8	180	2	19in	28in		Parallel
1902	100	4–6–0	6 8	200	2	$18\frac{1}{2}$in	30in	21,733	Parallel
1903	98	4–6–0	6 8	200	2	18in	30in	20,530	No 1–$\frac{1}{2}$ taper
1904	102	4–4–2	6 8	227	4	340mm 560mm	640mm 640mm	23,700	Parallel
1904	171	4–4–2	6 8	225	2	$18\frac{1}{2}$in	30in	23,090	No 1–Full taper
1905	103/4	4–4–2	6 8	227	4	360mm 600mm	640mm 640mm	27,000	Parallel
1906	40	4–4–2	6 8	225	4	$14\frac{1}{4}$in	26in	25,090	No 1–$\frac{1}{2}$ taper
1912	4000	4–6–0	6 8	225	4	15in	26in	27,800	No 1–Full taper
1929	4000	4–6–0	6 8	225	4	16in	26in	31,625	No 8–Full taper

CHAPTER TWO

THE PAGET LOCOMOTIVE

This project, described as an 'heroic experiment', was the only instance of a locomotive being built in a railway works and financed by an employee of that railway.

The Midland Railway, although the largest of the pre-grouping railways, had always been a 'small engine' line which involved a lot of double heading, particularly for freight traffic, and Paget's design for a general-purpose 2–6–2 was intended to overcome this problem.

Cecil W. Paget was the works manager at Derby under R. M. Deeley in 1904 when the design was started, and he probably thought that he could get the job done fairly cheaply in the way works costs can be adjusted by those in whose hands they lay. Unfortunately on Deeley's retirement in 1909 Paget was made general superintendent of the traffic department, and so lost control of the building costs of his locomotive No 2299. It was found to require about £2,000 more than Paget could afford in order to complete and test, and this extra money was provided by the Midland on the understanding that it became a railway project.

If Deeley had still been the mechanical engineer it might have been given a better reception, as he probably initially approved the project, but his successor Henry Fowler and the rest of the top echelon at Nelson Street, Derby, had little sympathy for the whole thing, which was known locally as 'Paget's Folly'. In retrospect it might almost be called 'Bulleid Beware'.

The design embraced two novel features – eight cylinders 18in diameter by 12in stroke driving on all three of the coupled axles, and a firebox completely lined with firebricks. The latter feature seems to have been quite successful, but it has never been repeated in any later boiler designs.

The multi-cylinder idea was apparently based on the Willans central valve engine at that time used in the railway works generating station at Derby. The Willans engine was notably reliable, quiet and easy to maintain; it was also known as the engine that had made the generation of electricity a commercially viable proposition.

These engines built at the Willans & Robinson works at Rugby (which later as part of English

The Paget locomotive, Midland Railway 8-cylinder 2–6–2 No 2299. *BR/OPC*

Electric, was to build the 1,600hp diesel engine for the LMS No 10000) were constructed to close tolerances of interchangeability, and it had been shown that it was possible completely to replace the central valve within a lunch hour. Unfortunately, this cardinal feature of the engine was dropped in favour of a rotary valve, no doubt because the Willans valve system could not have been adapted to the variation in speed and cut-off demanded by locomotive requirements. Rotary and sleeve valves have not been a great success, as Daimler subsequently found in its application to the internal combustion engine. Paget might have been more fortunate if he had adopted the conventional 'D' or piston valve operated by external eccentrics. However, 'might have beens' never work, so we will consider the details as actually constructed.

Paget had originally intended the locomotive to be built as a 4–6–0, but this was altered to a 2–6–2 probably to reduce the distance from the cylinders to the smokebox, and because without a trailing wheel, the rear cylinders would have been right under the firebox; a Pacific would have been too long for the turntables then in use on the Midland system.

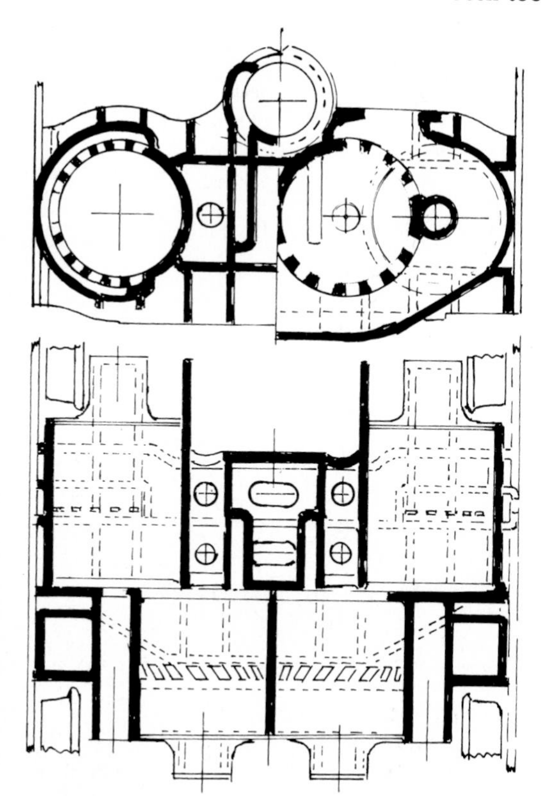

Cylinder arrangement

The eight cylinders were laid out to drive on all three coupled axles, two on the front axle, four on the centre and two on the rear axle. This meant three cranked axles, which must have considerably increased the cost, though this has never been disclosed. Paget presumably budgeted for around £3,000 which would have been the cost of a conventional 6-coupled tender engine at that date. As he ran out of his intended funding the cost would have amounted to nearly £5,000, considerably more than the GWR No 40 which was reputed to have been the most expensive main line locomotive in the UK at the time of its construction.

The steam chest supplying the eight cylinders was mounted centrally above each set of cylinders, and the steam was supplied to the cylinders via the rotating valve gear mounted inside the steam chest and driven from a gearbox mounted underneath the cab. The drive to the gearbox was by means of a cross shaft, itself driven by crank arms coupled to the rear driving wheels.

The cylinders were of the uniflow type, single-acting, with peripheral exhaust ports, and there may well have been considerable back pressure to the rear cylinders when the front ones were exhausting, but the layout of the exhaust piping is not very clear from the drawings available. It had originally been intended to arrange the valves vertically between each set of cylinders and for these to have been driven by chains from the centre and rear driving axles, but chain drives in an atmosphere of grit, ashes and brake block dust are not the best of devices on a steam locomotive!

The arrangement finally adopted was the result of prolonged testing over a year or more in order to test steam-tightness and wear rates; during those tests it was found that the rotary valves would absorb about 30 percent more power than the conventional D slide valve then in use on the standard Midland freight locomotives.

The valve casing and the valve itself were made of cast iron, but the ported liner was made of bronze and it was the differential expansion of these materials that was the main cause of the trouble with this gear. Initially it was fairly steam-tight, but after operation at speed considerable leakage took place past the valve, and a stop of some 15 minutes was necessary in order to restore clearances to dimensions suitable for operation. This would have been quite unacceptable in

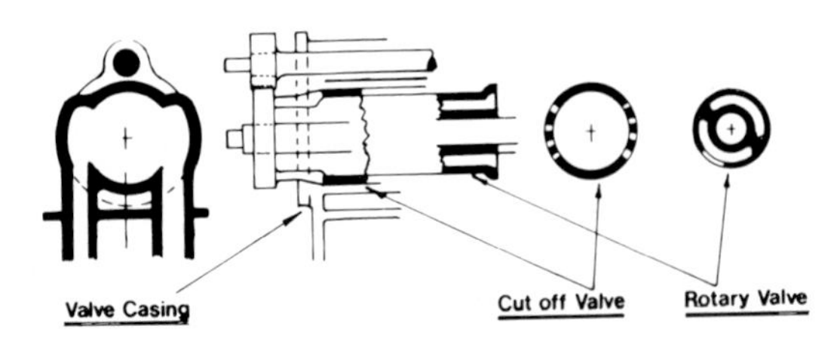

PAGET LOCOMOTIVE VALVE GEAR

normal service. At the time this was considered to be due to distortion of the valve due to friction with the liner, and time did not permit of the solution of this problem.

The liner could be rotated in the valve casing so as to vary the number of ports available for the passage of steam, and the cut-off percentages obtained were estimated as follows:

4 ports available	75 percent stroke
3 ports available	59 percent stroke
2 ports available	42 percent stroke
1 port available	26 percent stroke

The liners were rotated by the notch-up shaft operated by a steam and a water cylinder, remotely controlled by a small handle in the cab, conveniently mounted for the drivers' control. The operating cylinders were mounted on the front of the main cylinder assembly.

The gearbox for the drive to the rotating valves was mounted as shown in Fig. 7 under the cab and driven by a cross-shaft coupled by crank arms to the rear driving axle. In order to allow for the movement of the rear axle relative to the gearbox cross-shaft, a flexible ball joint was provided in the coupling rod between these two shafts. The gearbox contained the gearing for the right-angle drive to the valve shaft, and an epicyclic gear which enabled the valves to be reversed. The reversing was controlled by a handwheel mounted vertically in the drivers' cab by the lookout window and was power-assisted by a steam cylinder.

Paget had been an operating man and his designs included everything possible to make life easy for the footplatemen. The gearbox was made by David Brown & Co Ltd of Huddersfield, which

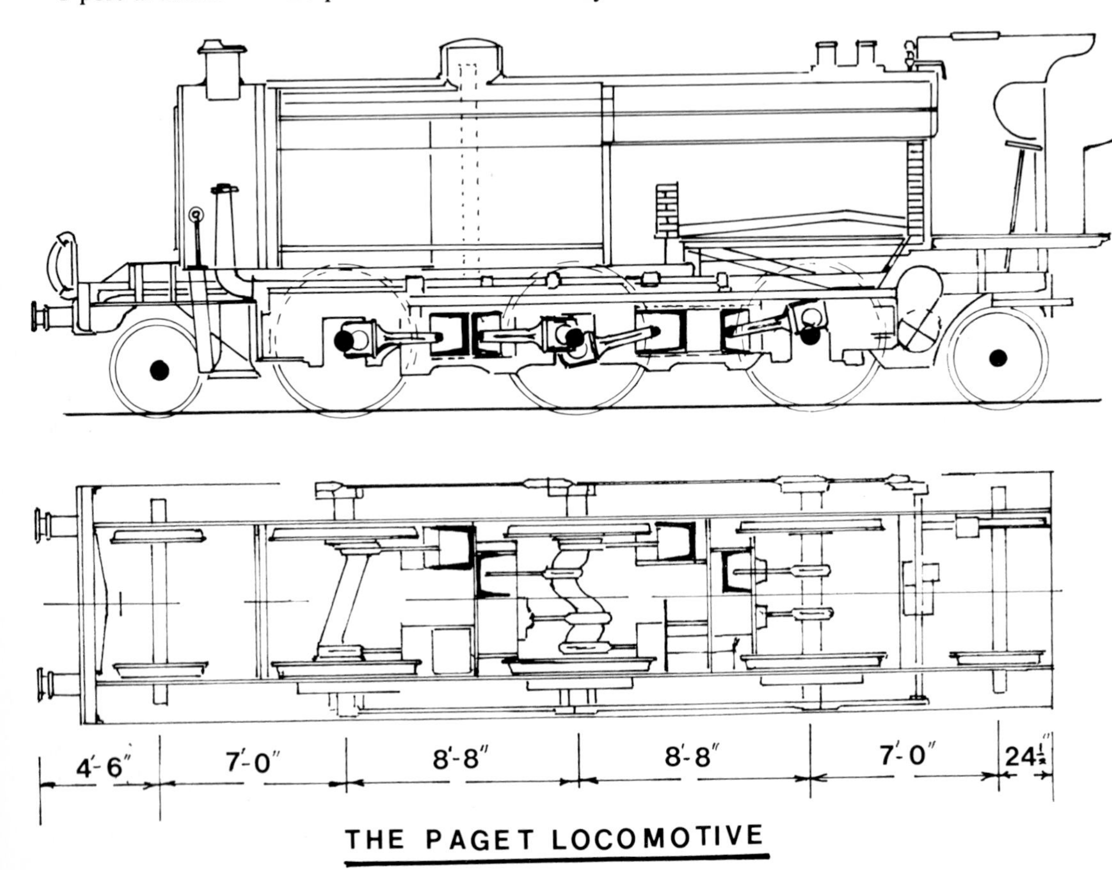

THE PAGET LOCOMOTIVE

also later supplied the gears for the Fell diesel-mechanical locomotive built at Derby in 1950.

The pistons were of the trunk type similar to those in use in internal combustion engines to-day; the front pistons were 19in long with three ring grooves, and the rear pistons were 13in long with two ring grooves. The piston rings were described as being of the Rowan type, and as the cylinders were open at the connecting rod ends there was a continual leakage of steam past the rings; this created an atmosphere of steam mist around and under the boiler, except when travelling at speed.

The connecting rods were of a conventional locomotive type with brass bearings for both large and small ends, and as the rotative speed at 80mph would have been 420rpm these gave no trouble and would probably have been satisfactory in service.

The basic mechanical construction was conventional with outside frames and ample bronze axleboxes 8½in diameter by 10in long. The two-wheel pony trucks were of the swing bolster two-pin central type with 3ft 3½in diameter wheels. As mentioned earlier, the three driving axles were all different, the leading axle having two crankthrows each close to the wheels; the rear axle also had two throws nearer the centre line, and the centre axle had four throws being driven by cylinders before and behind it. These three axles were forged by Messrs Rixon of Sheffield.

The balancing was virtually perfect and the running almost completely free of vibration. In spite of axle loads of 18.7 tons of the two outer driving axles, there is no record of any objection from the civil engineer to these weights. The total weight of the engine and tender in working order was 122.9 tons.

The other truly novel feature of the locomotive was the firebox which was constructed of steel and lined at the back and sides with 6in of firebricks. The firebox was nearly as long as the boiler, being 11ft 10½in overall, while the boiler shell was 12ft 0in between the tubeplates and 6ft 8in diameter. 9ft from the backplate was a cross-bridge of firebrick 9in thick from which heat was transferred via the firebridge support to heat the incoming air to the firebars. The firebox stays as well as the firetubes and the stay tubes were all of steel, thus eliminating any copperwork with its costly maintenance; the tubes and stay tubes were all ribbed internally to increase the heat transfer rates.

The area of the firegrate at 55sq ft was the

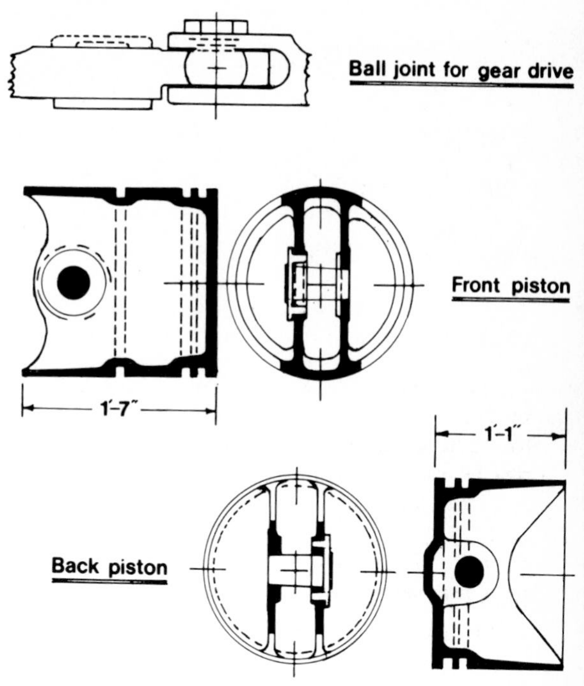

THE PAGET PISTON DETAILS

largest of any locomotive used in the UK, being 5sq ft larger than that of the LMS Coronation class. The largest up to the time of the Paget was that of the Holden 'Decapod' which was 42sq ft.

Two Chatwood firedoors were provided, but even so it must have been a bit of a problem for firemen not used to such a large grate area. Water nozzles were provided for sluicing-out the ashpan bottom, and two hoppers 13in diameter were fitted through which the ashes were emptied. There was also a special chute for emptying the ashes from the smokebox, so eliminating dirty jobs was evident on the part of the designer.

In spite of the novelty of the boiler design it proved completely successful in service in spite of the occasional loose firebrick. Had it been longer in service and proved reliable and economical, some of these ideas might have found their way into regular boiler construction.

Unfortunately there are no records of any performances by No 2299, but it probably never went for any longer run than the usual initial test run from Derby to Trent Junction, where it would have been turned round the triangle. Its tractive effort would have been around 28,600 lb, which would have meant 23 percent of the adhesive weight, quite adequate for any duties then called for by the Midland Railway.

The trials were primarily to test and perfect the

very novel valve gear, and the first problem was seizing-up of the ported bronze sleeve controlling the cut-off. Due to the larger expansion of this component, and to the extra steam pressure, the lubrication was inadequate and the sleeve seized in the casing. When the outer diameter of the sleeve was reduced to allow for this expansion the steam blew straight through to exhaust until the whole warmed up.

Eventually the sleeve was reduced to a clearance suitable for the maximum temperature when stationary, the steam pressure and centrifugal force being relied on to complete a seal when in motion. This finally did work and speeds up to 82mph were achieved, but with no record as to the weight of train. Since this speed must have been with passenger stock, the train weight was probably around 250 to 300 tons. Unfortunately on one Sunday test run in 1912 the whole sleeve and valve assembly seized-up solid when running at around 70mph near Syston. The main line to London was blocked for seven hours, which caused any further testing to be abandoned. There is a further similarity here to the Fell diesel which also seized-up on the main line to London, but a bit further away, at Kettering.

No 2299 was withdrawn and laid-up in the paint shop at Derby Works until 1918, when it was scrapped while Paget was in France commanding the Royal Engineers Railway Operating Division.

The Pagets do not seem to have been lucky in their engineering exploits, as the supercharged 4½-litre Bentley was financed some 15 years later by the Hon Dorothy Paget. This version, built much against the wishes of W. O. Bentley, is the one most favoured by present-day model kits and was driven principally by Sir Henry Birkin. Apart from holding the Brooklands lap record it was remarkably unsuccessful in its racing career and led to Bentley's financial plight; this caused Bentley to be bought-out by Rolls Royce and moved from Cricklewood to Derby.

CHAPTER THREE

TURBINE CONDENSING LOCOMOTIVES

By 1910, when the first of the turbine condensing locomotives to be tried out in the UK was built by the North British Locomotive Company, the condensing steam turbine was well established for use in power stations and in ships. The condenser was a vital component in order to achieve anything like a reasonable efficiency and thus economical operation. The condenser combined with the turbine was an ideal combination, because the large exit area required for steam when expanded to 27in of vacuum was more suited to a turbine design than to a reciprocating engine, and the turbine could exhaust straight into the condenser on which it was mounted. When the system was applied to a locomotive the condenser had to be mounted further away from the turbine, thus largely nullifying the benefit of the whole system. Even so, it was thought that it should be possible by using this system to improve on the low efficiency obtained with conventional cylinders exhausting direct to atmosphere, and this was obviously the hope of the builders of this type of locomotive.

The other objection with regard to condensing type locomotives is the lack of blastpipe effect, which itself is largely responsible for the high steam outputs obtainable with the relatively small boiler that can be fitted within the confines of most railway loading gauges.

The first of these locomotives to be built in the UK was a 4–4–0 + 4–4–0 turbo-electric unit constructed by the North British Locomotive Company, which had four 275hp electric traction motors and the turbo-generator mounted above floor level between the boiler and the condenser. In order to supply the traction motors fitted, the capacity of the turbine should have been around 1,600hp, but this figure cannot be confirmed, and in view of the boiler size is unlikely to have been sustained for long. There is no record of any operation, and the outbreak of war in 1914 probably put a stop to any possible development.

It was apparently dismantled and rebuilt in 1924 as a 4–4–0 + 0–4–4 using a geared drive system with two turbines, one on each bogie. These were compounded with a high pressure turbine on one bogie and a low pressure one on the other. Each turbine was rated at 500hp and the locomotive should have given up to 700 drawbar horsepower at 60mph, quite sufficient to pull a

North British Reid–Ramsey 4–4–0 + 4–4–0 as originally built. *Mitchell Library*

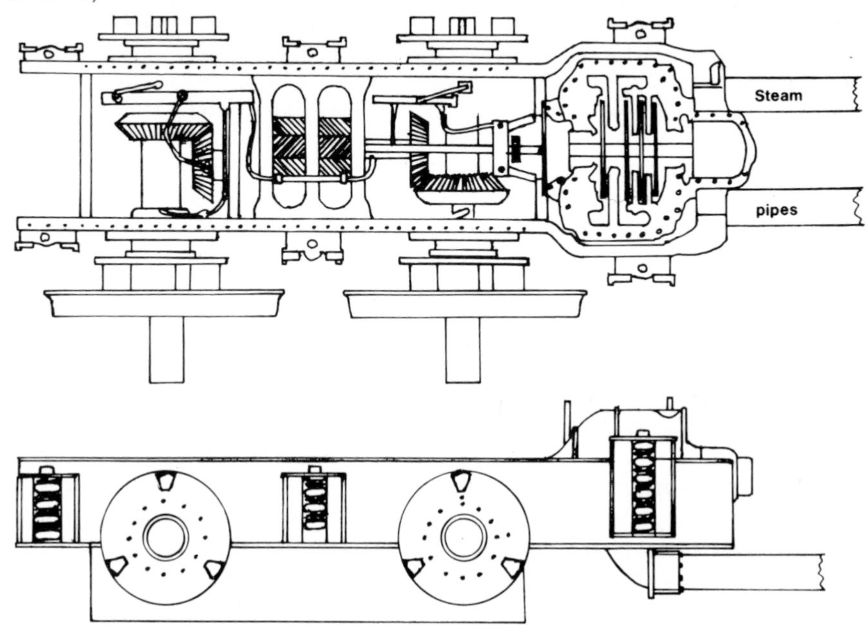

(*Above*) High pressure driving unit

(*Below*) Reid–McLeod turbine-electric 4–4–0 + 0–4–4 at the Atlas Works, on load tests. In the cab is James McLeod, and on the ground (from left) are A. Cooper and A. Patrick (draughtsmen), A. Mair and J. Moffat (fitters), J. Caldwell (driver), and L. Rankine (leading fitter). *Mitchell Library*

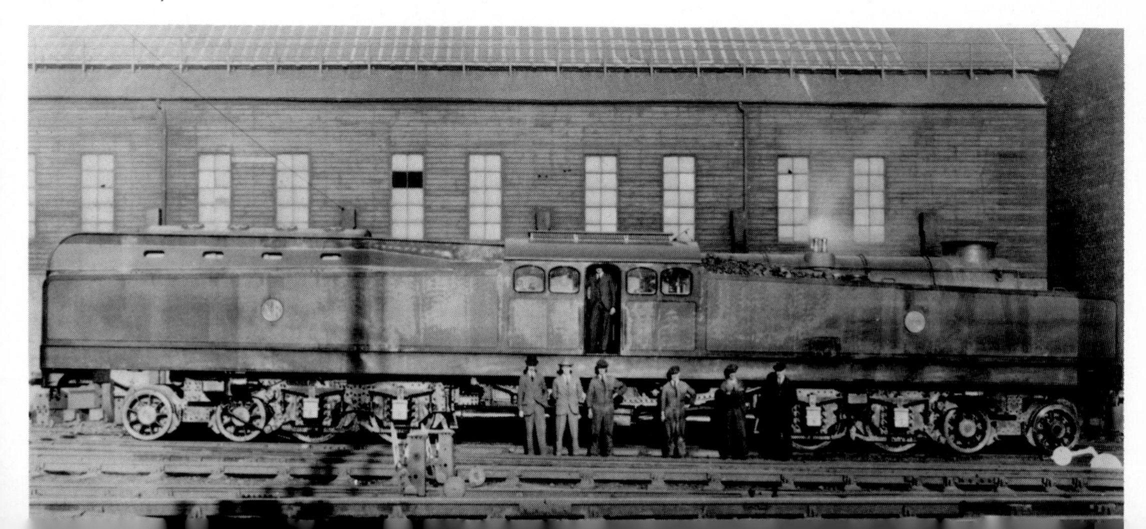

300-ton train at express speeds, but this does not appear to have been achieved.

This locomotive was a very handsome unit and was exhibited at the British Empire Exhibition at Wembley in 1924, where it was much admired by those who saw it (including the author). A large proportion of the first locomotive was re-used in the rebuild which was numbered 23141, including the main frame, the bogies and the boiler shell. The boiler pressure and temperature were 180 lb/sq in and 700°F, thus incorporating 320°F of superheat which was unlikely to have been used in the original model.

No 23141 was built under patents of Sir Hugh Reid and James McLeod and was known as the Reid-McLeod Steam Turbine Locomotive. It was the only 100 percent British designed and built model out of all the turbine jobs until the English Electric gas turbine GT3. Unfortunately this does not say much for the British share of this rather ephemeral market.

In No 23141 each bogie-mounted turbine was coupled to the driving wheels through double-reduction gearing, first through opposed helical gears with a ratio of 8 to 1, and then through right-angle bevel gears with a ratio of 2.38 to 1, giving an overall ratio of 19 to 1. With driving wheels of 4ft 0in diameter, a turbine speed of 8,000rpm corresponded to 60mph, but it is doubtful if this speed was ever achieved.

The steam for ahead admission passed through two 3in double-beat valves, and that for reverse through one 4in valve. From the high-pressure turbine the steam then passed through specially jointed pipes to the low-pressure unit and thence to the condenser, again through pipes flexible enough to allow for the bogie movement. Unfortunately, no details of this are available.

The condenser was of the air-cooled evaporative type using copper tubes divided into two groups, first ascending to a header and then descending to the bottom header from which the condensate was discharged to a hot well situated under the cab floor. A steam turbine-driven fan drew air over the tubes which were further cooled by spray from jets also drawn out by the turbine fan. These jets could be controlled by the driver to suit the operating conditions. The locomotive was designed to run with the condenser leading, to assist the air flow over the tubes.

The condensate, after passing to the hot well, was drawn from there by a boiler feed pump which delivered it to the boiler through a feed water heater. The exhaust steam from the various auxiliary pumps and fans also returned to the hot well.

The turbine casings were incorporated in the bogie framework with three blade rings for the forward operation and one for reverse, giving respectively 500hp ahead and up to 350hp in reverse. Both turbines were of the impulse type and were coupled direct to the two-stage reduction gearbox. Another auxiliary was a forced-draught steam-driven fan supplying air to the ashpan at $4\frac{1}{2}$in of water gauge pressure. When the fire door was opened by the fireman this forced air was diverted direct to the chimney, to prevent a blowback through the fire door. This forced-draught fan was started when the boiler pressure reached 90 lb sq in, and seven minutes later the full boiler pressure of 175 lb sq in was available.

On initial test a tractive effort of 15,000 lb was recorded by a dynamometer at the Hyde Park Works, and a freight train of 280 tons was easily manoeuvered in both directions. Track trials took place in March 1926 and April 1927 on the former the North British Railway line between Glasgow and Edinburgh with just two coaches. The first run had to be abandoned at Greenhill due to trouble with the circulating pumps and axlebox troubles beset the second trial, although it did get as far as Edinburgh. There it had to be assisted round the Haymarket loop, and suffered a turbine failure on the return run to Glasgow. As far as is known it never ran again. This was the first of the North British Locomotive Company's ventures into the

The Reid–McLeod locomotive is depicted here as No 23141, at Edinburgh (Waverley) station. *Mitchell Library*

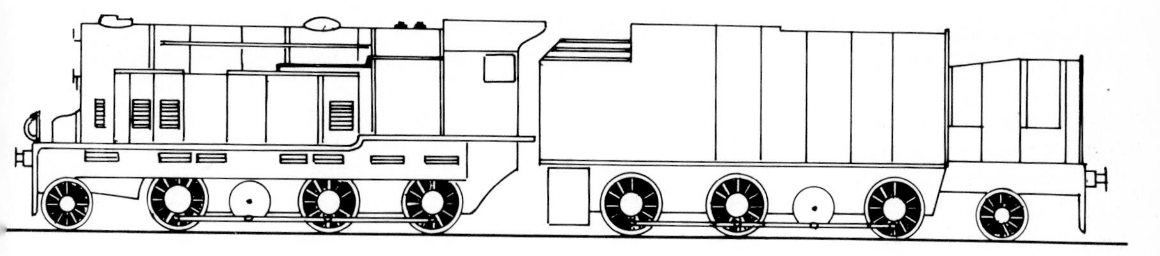

THE ARMSTRONG-WHITWORTH TURBO-ELECTRIC LOCOMOTIVE

unknown and it must have cost it least £15,000.

No 23141 was scheduled to appear at the centenary celebrations of the Stockton & Darlington Railway in July 1925, but it never arrived to take its place among the 54 working exhibits of all ages.

While the North British Locomotive Company was rebuilding its original model, another firm bitten by the turbine bug was Sir W. G. Armstrong-Whitworth of Scotswood Works, Newcastle-on-Tyne which also was talked into the turbo-electric venture. On this occasion it built a 2–6–6–2 (maker's number 160) using four electric motors and a jackshaft drive system with two motors geared to each jackshaft, and this was delivered to the Lancashire & Yorkshire Railway at Horwich on 20 March 1922. This was a two-unit machine with rigid wheelbase drive units as shown above. One unit carried the boiler, and the other fuel, turbo-generator and condenser.

The turbine was of the impulse-compound multi-stage design, directly coupled to the main generator running at 3,600rpm and delivering 890kW at 600V 3-phase. The four traction motors were rated at 275hp each and were presumably of the AC commutator type. The steam pressure was 200lb/sq in, with 300°F of superheat.

There seems to have been some confusion over the weight, since this was quoted on the manufacturer's diagram as 121.6 tons with a maximum axle load of 17 tons, then later as 130.8 tons with an axle load of 18 tons, but when weighed at Horwich it was found to be 156.2 tons with an axle load of 24 tons. Whether the builder ever weighed it before despatch is not known, but how the firm expected to get away with that discrepancy is amazing.

This weight problem almost ruled out any operation at all, but the civil engineer was persuaded to allow the locomotive to go as far as Bolton, where it ran on 5 April 1922. The forced-draught system was very unsatisfactory, resulting in poor combustion, and with a condenser vacuum of only 20in instead of the $27\frac{1}{2}$in designed; the coal and water consumptions were way above those hoped for.

A new chimney and brick arch improved the performance and 48mph was achieved with a train load of 230 tons. Some stationary tests on a water-brake dynamometer showed poor results below 30mph with only $25\frac{1}{2}$in of vacuum. A new condenser resulted in a saving of two tons total weight. Runs were then allowed on the main line between Wigan and Blowick, a distance of 15 miles; on 12 November 1922 the locomotive achieved 59mph with a load of 65 tons. The boiler pressure was no better than 170 lb/sq in and the coal consumption was over 40 lb/mile (about the same as the L&YR 4–6–0 with 400 tons).

The Armstrong–Whitworth turbo-electric locomotive at Manchester (London Road). *W. H. Whitworth/Rail Archive Stephenson*

Further runs took place on 13 May 1923 with 170 tons, when an average speed of 38mph was achieved, but the performance was not even as good as a standard Horwich 2–4–2 tank locomotive. The locomotive was then returned to Armstrong Whitworth and written-off. That must have cost the firm around £15–20,000 which it could ill afford at that stage when it had only just entered the locomotive business.

The third firm in the UK to produce a turbine condensing type of vehicle was Beyer Peacock Ltd of Gorton, Manchester which had entered into negotiations with Atkienbolaget Ljungström Anturbin of Sweden in November 1923. The Ljungström firm specialised in a contra-rotating turbine which consisted of only two sets of moving blades and was especially suitable for quick-starting purposes. However this type was not suitable for locomotive application and the company adopted the normal single shaft type for such duty.

In 1921 the firm of Nidquvist Holm had built a 4–6–6–2 (2–3–C–1) locomotive for the Swedish State Railway using a Ljungström 1500hp turbine, and produced figures showing a theoretical heat balance as:

Boiler loss	18 percent
Condenser fans	3.3 percent
Radiation loss	3.5 percent
Condenser loss	60.5 percent
Work output	14.7 percent

Tests undertaken in 1921 showed the following results:

Date	*Load tonnes*	*Coal consumption kg/1000 tonne km*	*Notes*
13–10–1921	505	12.2	
14–10–1921	492	14.1	
22–10–1921	540	11.6	
12–11–1921	475	—	Vacuum 26/27in water gauge Max speed 96kph.

(*Right*) Details of the turbine unit on the Beyer Peacock/Ljungström turbine-condensing locomotive. *North Western Museum of Science & Industry*

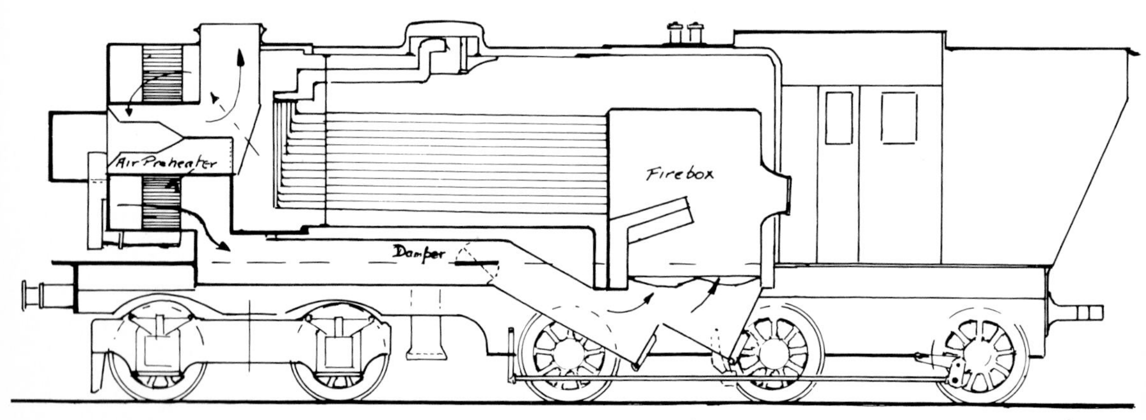

Beyer Ljungström turbine locomotive. Air flow to firebox

These performances seemed to justify Beyer-Peacock's intention to proceed with the design and manufacture of this type of locomotive, and on 2 January 1924 its Board (Minute 8) indicated the intention to purchase the Ljungström patent rights for £10,000. Incidentally, the Company overdraft at that time was just under £74,000.

The turbines and gears were ordered in April on a delivery promise of six months and in May an approach was made to George Hughes, the Lancashire & Yorkshire Railway chief mechanical engineer at Horwich, suggesting operation of the proposed locomotive on the newly constituted London Midland & Scottish Railway. The designs were submitted to Horwich in June, stated to be within the 1908 Bridge Curve, but in excess of that for the former Midland main line.

The design as shown below consisted of two vehicles similar to the Armstrong-Whitworth layout, except that the fuel and water were carried on the boiler unit. The turbine was coupled directly to the condenser, but there was a long and tortuous steampipe system from the boiler to the turbine through a flexible joint. To Beyer-Peacock this was nothing of a novelty as the layout had to be used in their double-ended designs of Garratt locomotives.

The turbine had a single-row impulse wheel followed by 18 rows of reaction blading and was designed for an output of 2,000hp at 10,500rpm, corresponding to a road speed of 78mph. The turbine was geared direct to the leading driving axle through triple-reduction gearing having an overall ratio of 25.2 to 1. The driving wheel diameter was 5ft 3in.

Another novel feature was an air preheater mounted integrally with the smokebox and designed to use the heat from the flue gases to heat the air on its way to the firebox. This preheater consisted of a rotating drum packed with thin steel plates driven by friction rollers coupled to a forced draught fan, which was required as there was no exhaust steam to the chimney and therefore no blastpipe effect. This preheater device probably contributed to the poor combustion that was a feature of the usual operation when in service. During the building period Ljungström suggested that a new material called 'Armco' be used for these preheater plates, presumably as the result of experience with the Swedish Railway unit though this was calculated to add 0.5 ton to the front bogie load.

The boiler steam conditions were designed to be 300lb/sq in with a superheat of 200°C., but the order for the Ross 'Pop' safety valves quoted 285 lb/sq in. Their cost was £10.5.0d (£10.25) each.

In March a lockout in the Swedish engineering industry delayed the delivery of the condenser tubes, but the official order had by then been placed on the works and vehicle numbers alloted as 421 for the boiler and 422 for the turbine drive unit. Locomotive number 6233 was given for the complete job.

The final design drawings showing weights and throw-over on curves had been sent to Horwich by

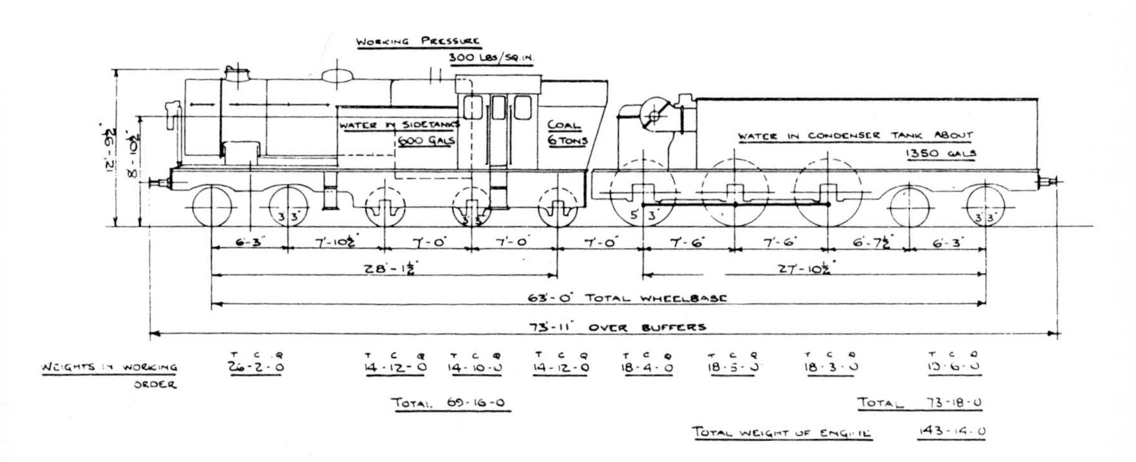

Works official picture of the Beyer Peacock/Ljungström locomotive. *North Western Museum of Science & Industry*

the company, but by October the locomotive control on the LMS had moved to Derby, and a letter was received from there requesting all the relevant data. This was sent off three days later, pointing out that all this had already been sent to Horwich. It was also pointed out that this locomotive had *not* been designed to run on the Midland section of the LMS. In spite of this, all the operation was carried out on the Midland lines, rather typical of the muddled state of locomotive affairs on the LMS in those days.

One June 22 1926 Board Minute No 11 reported completion of this locomotive, but no mention of the cost (Beyer-Peacock's overdraft by then was £158,000). On 4 July the first run took place from Gorton to Woodhead and back achieving a maximum speed of 45mph; on the 20 September the locomotive was handed-over to the LMS at Derby.

From then until the end of the year it was used on slow and semi-fast trains between Derby and Manchester. By December it seems that operational results were not showing great prospects as a Board decision was made not to take up the £10,000 option for patent rights, but to suggest future business on a royalty basis of £500 per locomotive.

In 1927 the operational range of the unit was increased to include fast trains from Derby to Birmingham and to London (St Pancras). A test run in May from Derby to Bedford with 13 coaches and a dynamometer car, weighing over 400 tons, gave a drawbar hp of 1,200 at a maximum speed of 76mph, but the fuel consumption was disappointing, being 57 lb/mile, 5.6lb/dbhp-hr. Poor combustion and the inability to maintain the vacuum were given as the reasons. The maximum turbine output was recorded as 1,650hp though this was designed for 2,000hp.

In February this locomotive had been offered to the Commonwealth Railway of Australia. Being a standard gauge line and with water problems across the Nullabor Plain, it was considered a particularly suitable area for this type of locomotive; perhaps luckily for the operating folk at Port Augusta nothing came of this.

During the latter part of 1927 it was returned to Gorton for modifications, but these do not seem to have made much improvement; a series of test runs in March and April 1928 did not show any better results.

These tests took place between Leeds (Stourton) and London (Somers Town) freight depots with 40 wagons, approximately 600 tons. On the first run from Leeds, delays of 27 minutes were noted due to shortage of steam on the 1 in 100 inclines out of Sheffield, caused by the damper in the air duct to the firebox falling shut; the final arrival was 47 minutes late. On the return run a defective wagon caused a delay of 38 minutes at Luton, but the final arrival was only five minutes late.

On 2 April a leak from the feed pump joint entailing a stop at Bedford to take water, lost 13 minutes, and on the return run next day a hot box at Kettering caused ten minutes delay, but nine of these had been made up on arrival at Leeds. It was noted that a large amount of black smoke was emitted on all lines indicating poor combustion. A summary of these results is given in Table 3.

Table 3

Results of tests with Beyer-Ljungström locomotive in March and April 1928

LEEDS (STOURTON) TO LONDON (SOMERS TOWN) VIA SHEFFIELD

Distance miles	*Booked time minutes*	*Journey times (minutes)* 28/3/28	2/4/28	11/4/28
193	326	374	339	332
Coal lb/mile		67.4	45	43
Coal lb/ton mile		0.112	0.076	0.072
Water gallons/mile		4.36	9.59	6.48

LONDON (SOMERS TOWN) TO LEEDS VIA NOTTINGHAM AND STAVELEY

Distance miles	*Booked time minutes*	*Journey times (minutes)* 29/3/28	3/4/28	12/4/28
198	352	357	353	354
Coal lb/mile		56	55	48
Coal lb/ton mile		0.089	0.089	0.087
Water gallons/mile		6.67	4.92	5.2

The turbine outputs and drawbar hp results were recorded as:

	Turbine hp	*DBHP*	*TE(lb)*
10mph	500	—	—
20mph	880	528	—
30mph	1030	618	7725
40mph	1056	643	—
50mph	960	576	—
60mph	760	456	2850

These results were then compared to those from a standard 2–6–0 freight locomotive which show up as follows:

LEEDS TO LONDON	*Ljungström*	*2–6–0*
Coal lb/ton mile	0.074	0.087
Water gallons/mile	7.96	42.3

LONDON TO LEEDS	*Ljungström*	*2–6–0*
Coal lb/ton mile	0.089	0.083
Water gallons/mile	5.71	42.7

The Ljungström locomotive saw main line service in 1926/7, and carrying express passenger headlamps it is depicted at Nottingham (Midland). *J. N. Hall/Rail Archive Stephenson*

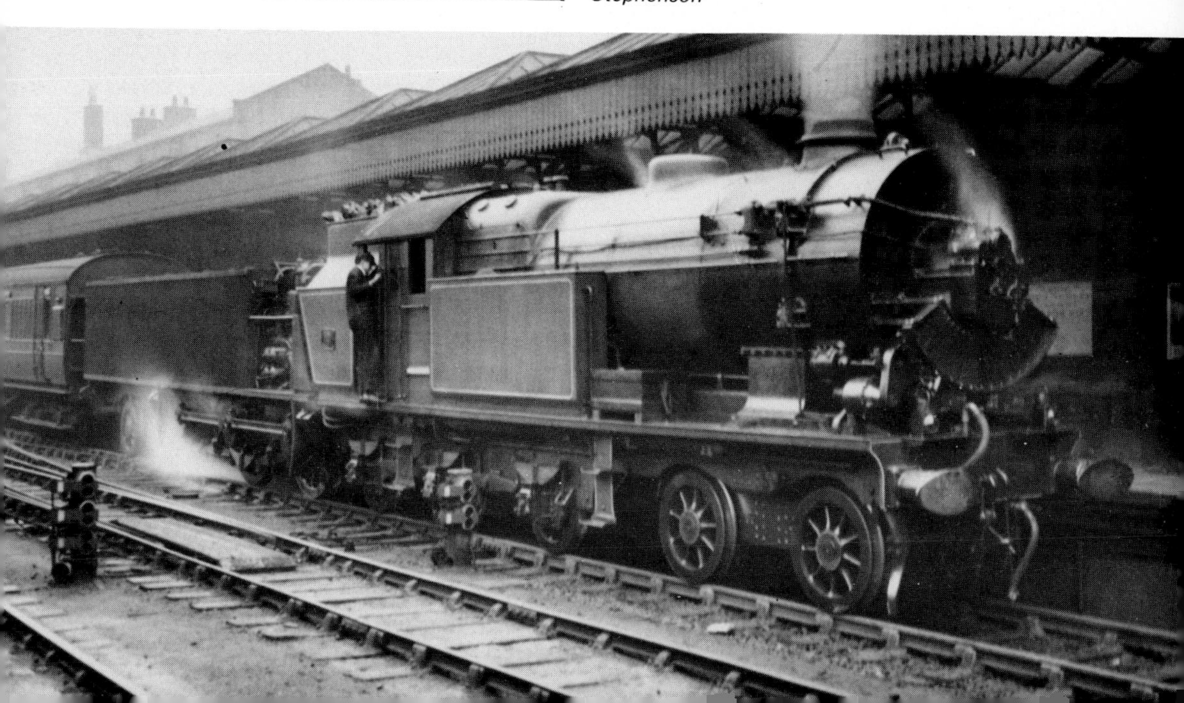

The results were not considered good enough to warrant any further testing or development and the unit was withdrawn. The whole locomotive was offered back to Ljungström for £30,000 in July 1928 so presumably this represents the expenditure on the project, but nothing seems to have come of this and it was dismantled. By then Beyer-Peacock's overdraft had reached £200,000. At the end of 1929 the firm received an order for 30 Garratt locomotives for the LMS, and as a result of this and other good overseas orders the overdraft was almost eliminated by 1930.

With the designed steam conditions of 300 lb/sq in and a superheat of 200°C combined with a vacuum of 27in, a theoretical overall efficiency of 27.6 percent should have been attainable at full load, but this was nowhere reached, as was shown by the operating results. Even if some of this loss in performance was due to condenser leaks, most of it seems to have been due to poor combustion, and for this the air preheater was probably largely to blame. As it relied on friction drive it was probably not rotating much of the time which would have caused the plates to foul up. There was no way the driver could tell if it was working properly when at speed and this might not have been obvious when in the depot.

One more Ljungström locomotive was put into service in Sweden in 1927 and remained in operation until 1939; that one probably influenced the building of the LMS Turbomotive which is considered later.

CHAPTER FOUR

The Kitson-Still Locomotive

The Kitson-Still could be called the most courageous of all the efforts in the 1920s to find and produce a more efficient motive power unit for railway traction. It was an attempt to combine the fuel-saving capability of the internal-combustion engine with the flexibility and high starting torque of the steam engine. As Lt Col Kitson Clark put it in his paper to the Institution of Mechanical Engineers 'Internal Combustion Locomotives' in 1927, the Still system impressed him by its unique combination of internal-combustion engine for continuous work, with steam for starting, overload and auxiliaries such as brakes and train heating.

This was very much an individually-inspired effort backed by only a small firm, and endeavouring to carry out a tremendous amount of fundamental development. Unfortunately to start with, the lesson of the abortive 1912 Sulzer-Borsig attempt to couple a diesel engine direct to the driving wheels had either been overlooked or ignored, see diagram below.

The diesel engine gives a virtually constant torque throughout its speed range and therefore can only give its maximum power output at full speed. This not only means a poor performance for most of its speed range, but also limits the top speed because of certain features in the design of the engine itself. Most of the pioneers working in the diesel field at that time appreciated that some form of intermediate transmission was necessary between the engine and the wheels so that the engine could be operated as near its full speed and output as possible throughout the variable speed range of the locomotive. For main line locomotive work the electrical transmission was to prove the most effective of all the systems tried, but at the

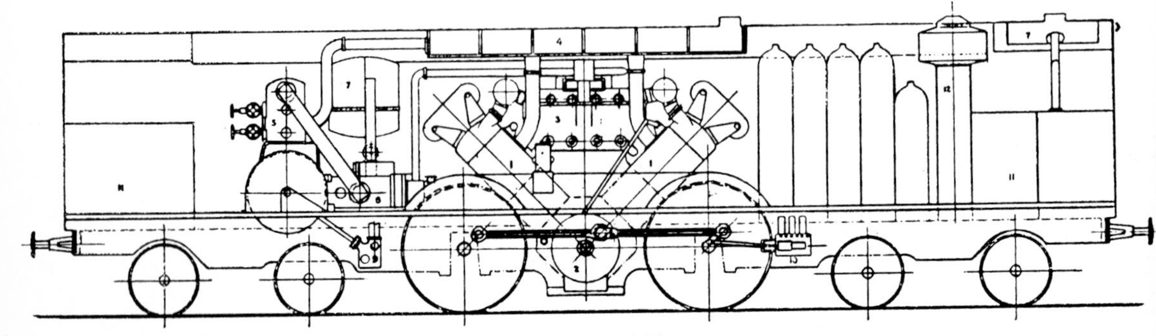

Layout of Sulzer-Diesel-Klose-Borsig locomotive completed in 1912

time the Kitson-Still was built this was far from being proven and there were many and varied systems still under trial.

The Still Engine Company had been operating a 400hp 2-stroke engine for around ten years at its Chiswick Laboratory and had obtained this output at a fuel rate of only 0.345 lb of oil per horsepower. This was an extremely good figure at that time, but it was amazing that it had never been taken-up commercially. It was appreciated that at least 1,000hp would be needed for the type of locomotive proposed, and that this would best be produced in a 4-stroke engine to avoid the complication of a compressor. To obtain an even torque with a 4-stroke engine, eight cylinders would be needed, and in order to attain the necessary starting tractive effort on the steam side, a cylinder diameter of 13.5in would be required. The piston stroke was then settled at 15.5in with an engine top speed of 450rpm, so it is difficult to see how the hoped-for output of 1,000hp could be obtained. This combination could only give around 800hp with a brake mean effective pressure of 80 lb/sq in, which is all that could be expected of a naturally-aspirated diesel engine of this type.

The engine was arranged with horizontally-opposed cylinders, four each side of a transverse four-throw crankshaft; the crankshaft was geared to a jackshaft through a flexible gear having a ratio of 1.878 to 1, giving a road speed of only 42.7mph at the top engine speed of 450rpm – a severe limitation when compared to an equivalent 2–6–2 conventional tank locomotive.

The diesel cylinders were on the outside, with opposed inlet and exhaust valves, the steam cylinders being on the crankshaft side fed through a Hackworth type valve gear giving cut-off variations between 65 percent and 6 percent.

There was not a lot of room left for the boiler within the British loading gauge. The boiler was thus 4ft 3in diameter by 9ft 0in between tubeplates, giving 563sq ft of evaporative surface with 508sq ft of regenerative surface and producing saturated steam at 180 lb/sq in. The oil-fired firebox was a simple corrugated drum which had no firegrate, stays or firebricks. This portion of the design was simple, cheap and light, requiring a lift of no more than six tons to handle any portion of the mechanism above the axles. Incidentally, this was not the first application of a corrugated firebox as these had been used by the Lancashire & Yorkshire Railway on some of its freight locomotives in 1902. The whole was mounted on a 2–6–2 (1-C-1) wheel arrangement with a total designed weight of 70 tons, but on production this came to 85 tons, with an axle load of 20.6 tons. The layout is shown below.

The driving wheel diameter was 5ft 0in and the pony wheels 3ft 0in diameter. The high-pitched boiler gave an unusual effect to the final appearance and perhaps bore out the maxim that if a design is right it looks right – somehow the Kitson-Still did not look right.

In order to prove the diesel engine side of the cycle, a single cylinder unit was built and coupled to a 15-ton flywheel, to simulate operating conditions. There was a separate oil-fired vertical boiler, and though this was not fed by the exhaust gas as it would be on the locomotive, it was

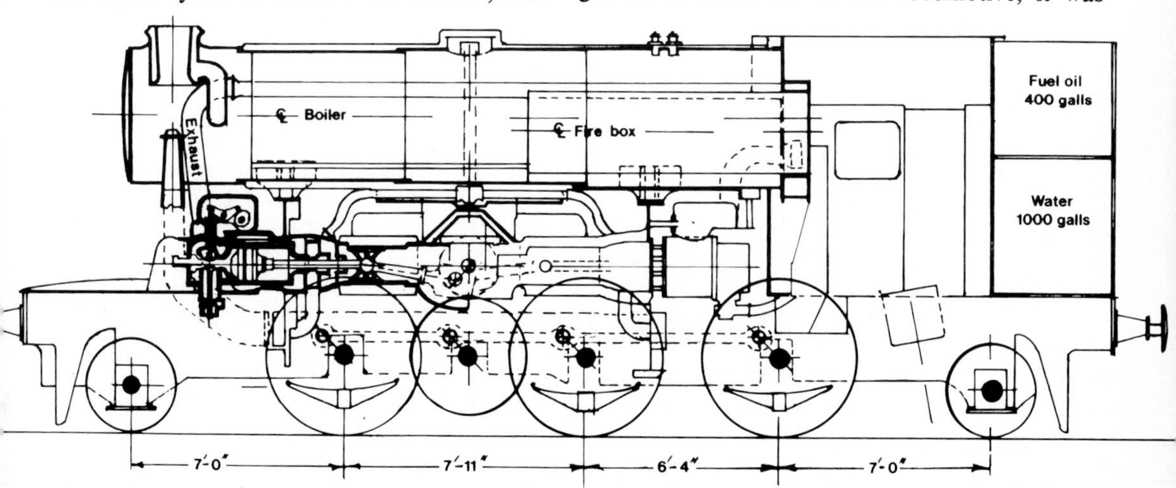

THE KITSON-STILL STEAM DIESEL LOCOMOTIVE

coupled to the jacket cooling system to make use of the heat rejected to the cylinder walls. Though all right in theory, this feature almost certainly caused operational problems, because this was an early attempt at what is now called 'vapour phase' cooling. This results in conditions much hotter than normal in the combustion area, and the lubricating oils at that date could not cope with those temperatures. The straight mineral oils then available would carbonise rapidly at these temperatures. There was no circulating pump for this cooling water, and the system worked on the thermo-syphon principle relying on the temperature difference between the top and bottom of the boiler. This could hardly have provided sufficient water flow and must account for one of the major problems in operation.

The main object of the single-cylinder test rig was to get the combustion right under all conditions of operation from 30rpm to 450rpm, and this was a formidable project at that time. Since it was intended to avoid the use of a compressor this obviated air injection, and a solid injection fuel pump was adopted. With any type of solid injection fuel pump the amount of fuel injected is dependent on the time of injection, and this is determined by releasing the pressure when the correct amount of fuel has been sent to the cylinder.

In the usual Bosch type injection pump the fuel measurement is achieved by means of a spiral in the plunger body. The point of release is determined by rotating a sleeve round the plunger to set this point as called for by the governor. On this Kitson-built engine the point of release was set by an auxiliary valve in the delivery line, actuated by a trip lever operated by the fuel pump cam. Since there was no governor, on this engine the trip lever setting was directly under the driver's control.

The fuel from the pump fed direct to an injector generally similar to those in use to-day, but part of the development was the inevitable trial and error of the number and angle of the fuel holes in the nozzle tip in order to achieve correct combustion.

Initially an injection pressure of 2,500 sq in, with three nozzle holes 0.024in diameter at an included cone of 19° was tried, but the smoke was black at all speeds. The injection pressure was then raised to 5,000lb/sq in and the holes enlarged to 0.026in, which resulted in improved combustion except at full output. Attempts were then made to improve the compression ratio by adding temporary blocks of various shapes to the piston crown.

After trying 232 combinations of blocks and nozzles, the combustion problem was finally overcome by re-designing the cylinder head itself. The new head had less clearance volume, with larger inlet and exhaust valves resulting in a BMEP of 80 lb/sq in being obtained at a fuel consumption of 0.36 lb/BHP hour. The actual injector nozzle design and the injector pressure required in order to obtain this result is not quoted, but as there was ten percent free oxygen in the exhaust this should have been fairly clear.

Reversing was achieved by the use of two sets of cams with a sliding camshaft, as was the practice on most 4-stroke marine engines before the advent of the reverse/reduction gearbox. This procedure entailed lifting the valves while the camshaft was moved from the forward to the reverse position and vice versa.

The crankshaft which was arranged athwart the main frame was made up of two twin-throw sections joined by central gearing. This gear drove on to a jackshaft below through a spring-loaded gear having a ratio of 1.878 to 1. The jackshaft was connected to the driving wheels through normal coupling rods.

The Hackworth steam valve gear was operated by crankarms at either end of the main crankshaft.

The oil-fired boiler comprised 119 tubes of 1.75in diameter by 9ft 0in long and a tubular corrugated firebox of 72sq ft heating surface, making a total of 562.6sq ft. The exhaust gas from the diesel engine passed into the regenerative surface through 36 tubes 2.75in in diameter and 17ft 4in long, those from the front cylinders also passing through two tubes of 6.5in diameter. This system also acted as a silencer for the diesel engine. The total heating surface area for the regenerative portion was 507.7sq ft.

There was no doubt too much optimism about how much use the diesel exhaust gas would be, but there were not many installations with waste gas boilers to go by at that time. Some simple calculations would have shown that not much more than 1.5lb of steam per hour per horse power could be obtained at full load and considerably less (about 0.5lb/hr) at half load. Also as the exhaust temperature from the diesel cylinders was around 600°F, the available heat would be miniscule compared with that from a firebox with a temperature of 1,800°F in a normal locomotive boiler. Even with a highly-rated modern diesel

The Kitson–Still 2–6–2 steam/diesel locomotive at Copley Hill LNER shed, Leeds.

engine, the waste heat recovery plant is often nearly as large as the engine itself; this was one of the reasons why this heat could not be used in passenger diesel locomotives for train heating purposes.

This locomotive was finally put together by Kitson of Leeds and was submitted to the London & North Eastern Railway for trials and evaluation. The first trials took place on the 29 April 1928 over routes between Leeds and Wakefield. The route selected seemed to be an arduous one, and whether this was at Kitson's suggestion or whether the LNER was attempting to kill it off is not known. The load was a six-wheeled observation car and six articulated coaches making a total load of 118 tons plus a fairly large party from both the builders and the LNER.

Two round trips were made, first the 9.50am ex-Leeds followed by the 11.10am ex-Wakefield. There were several delays due to the inevitable Sunday work on the line and the net losses due to the locomotive could be put at:

Run No 1 1 minute
Run No 2 3½ minutes
Run No 3 2½ minutes plus 5 mins late start
Run No 4 5 minutes

Some of the delays were due to getting stuck on dead centres, as the driver could not judge from the crank position of the coupling rods the position of the cylinder cranks owing to the gear ratio between them. It was also noted that the boiler was sometimes short of steam, but no readings were recorded nor were any fuel compositions noted. The details of these runs are set out in Table 4 and the route and gradient profile shown on page 32.

Following these tests the locomotive was returned to Kitson for modifications which included the fitting of power-assisted reverser gear to save time when getting away from a dead-centre start and increasing the maximum cut-off on the steam gear to 75 percent. The heating surface area of the regenerative side was increased to 640sq ft and the boiler pressure raised to 200 lb/sq in. Following these alterations, further runs were carried out between Darlington and Starbeck (Harrogate), with results recorded on the LNER dynamometer car on 27 September 1928.

On the first day when hauling 183 tons of passenger stock, a defect in the fuel pump put four cylinders out of action so that run had to be abandoned. On the next day with a train of freight stock weighing 403 tons the 39 miles were run in 107 minutes outwards (21.9mph) and 96 minutes return (24.4mph). The diesel engine fired at 5mph (53rpm), and 28 miles were run in either direction on the diesel engine only. When steam was used for

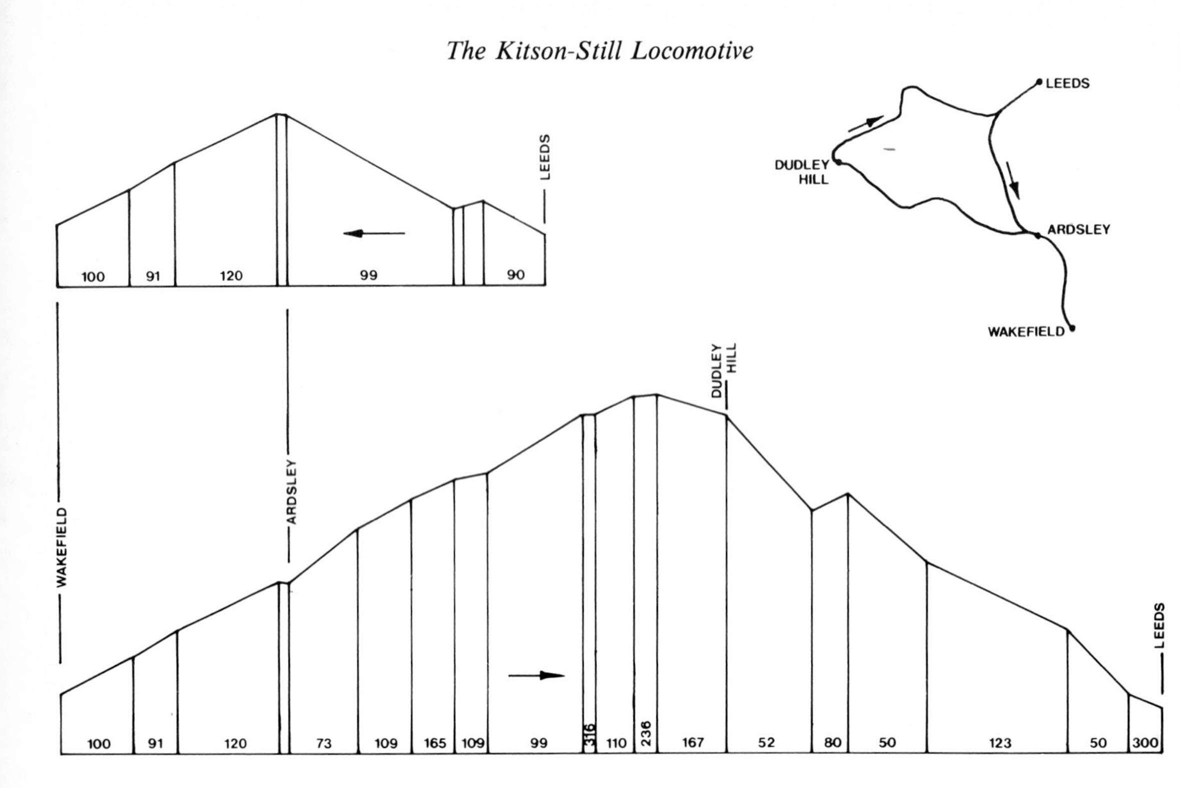

TEST ROUTE AND GRADIENT PROFILE LEEDS TO WAKEFIELD

assistance uphill, the boiler pressure fell rapidly from 204 lb/sq in down to 85 lb/sq in. The maximum speed also had to be limited to 40mph due to some weak valve springs on the diesel engine.

The next run took place on the 1 October with a freight train of 355 tons and the times were 98 minutes out (23.9mph) and 85 minutes back (27.5mph). The boiler performed slightly better, but the pressure still fell to 120 lb/sq in.

The last run of this series the next day was with 278 tons of passenger stock and the times were outward 85 minutes (27.5mph) and 71 minutes return (32.9mph). On this occasion the diesel engine operated alone for 33 out of the 39 miles and the boiler pressure did not fall below 135 lb/sq in. Some trouble was experienced with one of the diesel pistons, but the trip was completed. On inspection the piston was found to be badly scored, and the rings seized in their grooves, due no doubt to the deterioration of the oil as a result of overheating. The other major trouble was due to leakage of the expansion joints between the cylinder liner and the water jackets also due to the cooling system adopted.

The results of these tests are set out in Table 5, from which it can be deduced that the fuel consumption when on diesel engine operation was around 0.56 lb/bhp hr; this compares favourably with modern diesel locomotives. British Railways tests gave 0.65 lb bhp hr for the Southern Region No 10203 and 0.514lb/bhp hr for the Brush No D5000.

On 9 October 1928 some resistance measurements were taken by the dynamometer car on a run from Fighting Cocks to Darlington, a distance of 16.3 miles, in which the locomotive resistance was recorded as high as 47.0 lb/ton at 26mph. This compares with test figures of 12.7 lb/ton at this speed for the British Railways 4–6–2 No 71000, and 5.1lb/ton for the diesel-electric Bo-Bo D8000. This severe handicap, combined with the poor boiler performance, accounted for the inadequate results obtained from this locomotive.

Some further dynamometer car tests were carried out in August 1929, but there does not seem to be any trace of the results. Some five years later, in June 1933, the final runs took place with a class B freight between York and Hull. From York to Hull via Beverley with 363 tons an overall, fuel consumption of 13lb of oil per mile was noted giving a return of 1.57lb/bhp hr. On the return from Hull to York via Selby with 453 tons the consumption was again 13 lb/mile giving 1.26 lb/bhp hr. This compares with around 0.6 lb/bhp hr for a modern diesel electric locomotive.

Unfortunately, largely as a result of the time and money spent on this job, Kitson got into financial difficulties and had to pull out of the locomotive business. The factory was later turned to the production of McLaren diesel engines, some of which were used in locomotives; a large proportion found their way to the USSR as part of the mass production of McLaren 55kW diesel generator sets.

As a footnote it is nice to record that Lt Col Kitson Clark's book about the history of the Kitson Works was given the Literary Award by the Institution of Locomotive Engineers.

Table 4

Kitson-Still locomotive – initial runs Leeds to Wakefield

	Miles	*Non-stop schedule (minutes)*	*Actual time (minutes)*	*Locomotive loss (minutes)*	*Stopping schedule (minutes)*	*Actual time (minutes)*	*Locomotive loss (minutes)*
Leeds							5
Beeston	2.5		6	–1	8	14	1½
Ardsley	5.5	12	13	1	15	22	2
Wrenthorp Jn	9.2	22	25		27	32	–1
Wakefield	10.1	24	28	1	32	35	
Total loss due to locomotive		–	–	1	–	–	2½, plus 5 late start
Wakefield							
Ardsley	4.3	8	11	2½	10/11	12½/14½	3½
Tingley	5.8		15		15	19½/21½	3
Morley	7.0	15	19		19	25/26	½
Birkenshaw	10.9	19	28	5½	31	38/38½	– ½
Dudley Hill	12.8	22	31	–1	35	43/43½	1
Greenside	15.5	26	36	–3	41	48½/49	– ½
Holbeck	20.8	38	46		52/53	59½/60	–1
Leeds	21.3	40	48	– ½	55	61	–1
Total loss due to locomotive		–	–	3½	–	–	5

Table 5

Kitson-Still Locomotive Dynamometer Car Trials 1928

Details	*Dates* 28 Sep	28 Sep	1 Oct	1 Oct	2 Oct	2 Oct
Train weight tons	403	403	355	355	278	278
Journey time minutes	107	96	98	85	85	71
Average speed mph	21.9	24.4	23.9	27.5	27.5	32.9
IC engine miles	27.7	29.0	31.8	31.9	34.5	31.3
Steam pressure max lb/sq in	204	190	205	198	205	203
min lb/sq in	85	105	120	135	140	135
Diesel engine exhaust temp °F	590	633	554	512	610	656
Tractive effort max lb	12,110	13,440	10,080	10,080	8,290	6,720
Tractive effort IC Engine only – lb	5,380	3,800	5,750	6,270	2,910	4,030
Dbhp IC engine	288	279	267	283	272	330
Fuel lb/mile IC engine	7.6	5.4	6.6	5.2	6.3	5.6
Steam boiler	20.9	16.4	15.0	9.8	10.9	11.3
Fuel lb/Dbhp hr	0.58	0.47	0.59	0.50	0.64	0.56

CHAPTER FIVE

The First No 10000

The North Eastern Railway dynamometer car, which had been built as a copy of the Swindon version, was first used on a test run on 6 March 1906 when testing the company's locomotive No 2109 in conjunction with the new East Coast Joint stock. The first test run with one of the Gresley Pacifics was on 25 June 1923 with No 1472.

The coal consumption of these early Pacifics was enormous until the footplate staff learned how to handle them. From drivers' descriptions they could use a tenderful of coal on a run from Grantham to London and back, over 80 lb of coal per mile. By 1925 at the time of the Interchange Trials with the GWR, Castle Class the consumption was down to around 55 lb per mile with a 500-ton train.

At the rates quoted a Pacific on a non-stop run from London to Edinburgh would consume nearly ten tons of coal – the standard LNER tender only held eight tons. In an attempt to improve on this performance Nigel Gresley considered the use of higher boiler pressures, and in view of the close connection between Darlington and naval boiler practice as used in ships built on the North East coast, the idea of using the Yarrow water tube type of boiler was formulated.

It was obviously not appreciated that a water tube boiler when mounted on a rigid base such as a power station or a ship's engine room, with proper facilities for expansion, is very different to the mountings on a lively chassis such as a locomotive frame. However, after three years of design and negotiation the design was finalised in 1927 and the order placed with Yarrow early in 1928.

This design consisted of four low-level water drums, two each side at the rear, connected by curved tubes to a single steam drum at the top operating at 450lb/sq in. Owing to the height of the top drum, a conventional chimney could not be fitted and a taper design was adopted at the front, with a single chimney. This was the result of wind tunnel tests carried out by Professor W. E. Dalby, as shown in the diagram top right.

The boiler was tested at the Yarrow works at Glasgow in October 1929 and ran for four hours at an output of 20,000 lb of steam per hour at 450 lb/sq in. The coal rate is not mentioned, though tests on one of the conventional Gresley Pacific boilers at 220 lb/sq in and the same steaming rate, gave a coal consumption figure of 2,757 lb/hr. Assuming a calorific value of 13,000BTH/lb for the coal, and a boiler efficiency of 80 percent this would have meant a direct emission from the chimney of nearly 12,000hp. The continuous roar of such an exhaust was probably accepted as normal in a boiler works such as Yarrow's, but when carried out at Darlington within half a mile of domestic housing, some serious complaints resulted. This would have been the nearest thing in those days, to an aircraft jet engine.

The initial boiler test had resulted in a steam temperature of 900°F and the superheater

General diagram of No 10000 as originally built.

(*Right*) Cross section views of No 10000. *National Railway Museum*

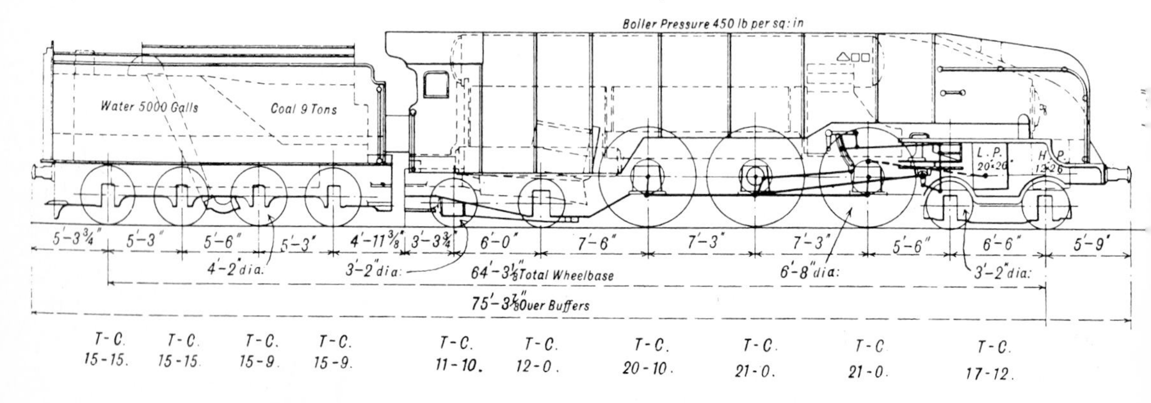

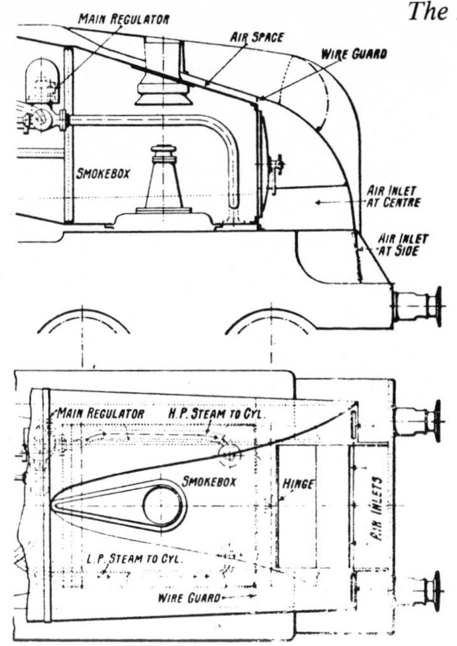

No 10000 First build

elements were then shortened to reduce this to 700°F.

The 'Hush-hush' engine, as it was known, was built at Darlington and had six driving wheels of 6ft 8in diameter, a standard leading bogie and two trailing axles; the first of these had radial movement in the frame and the second was on an independent triangular frame. These trailing axles were required in order to accomodate the extra boiler length.

There were two inside high-pressure (hp) cylinders, 12in diameter (later reduced to 10in) by 26in stroke driving the front axle, and two outside low-pressure (lp) cylinders 20in diameter by 26in stroke driving the centre axle. External Walschaert valve gear drove the low-pressure valves, and from their rocking shafts actuated the internal high-pressure valve gear; The cut-offs of the high-pressure and low-pressure cylinders could be adjusted independently.

The boiler heating surface was 2,126sq ft, with a grate area of 34.95sq ft; The weight in working order was 103.6 tons compared to the 96 tons of

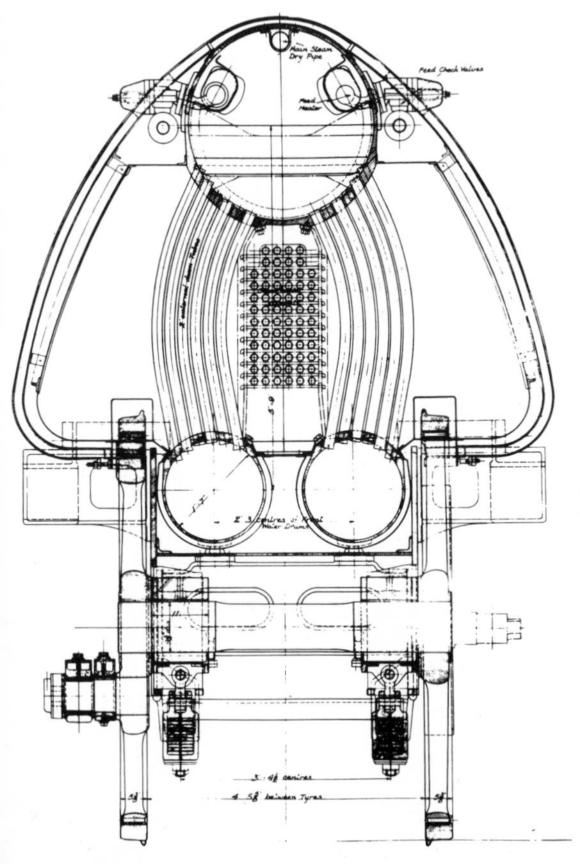

Section through intermediate wheels

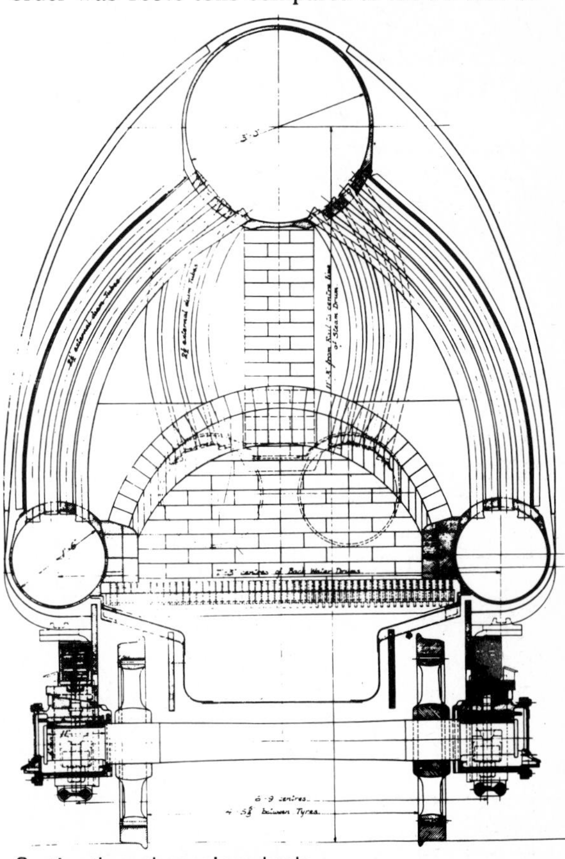

Section through carrying wheels

The "hush-hush" locomotive No 10000 at Grantham in 1930, on the up Flying Scotsman. (Note the Great Northern somersault signal with blastplate at the bottom of the post.) *T. G. Hepburn/Rail Archive Stephenson*

the standard Pacifics. No 10000 was completed at Darlington in December 1929 and ran its first trial outing on 12 December. On its first test run with 350 tons on 30 January 1930 from Darlington to York and back the steaming results were most unsatisfactory, with a fall in pressure to 230lb/sq in during the first 15 minutes.

Logged results from Darlington to York (with similar results on the return run) were as follows:

Time	*Boiler pressure*	*High-pressure chest*	*Cut-Off hp*	*Cut-Off lp*	*Low-pressure chest*	*Front flue temp*	*Smoke box vacuum*
	lb/sq in	*lb/sq in*	*%*	*%*	*lb/sq in*	*°F*	*in*
11.00	390	305	72	72	75	624	1½
11.05	320	250	30	70	45	880	2½
11.10	260	195	28	70	30	890	1½
11.15	230	175	28	68	28	880	1½
11.20	288	OFF	–	–	–	770	1
11.25	340	300	28	65	50	730	3½
11.30	340	290	20	58	43	970	3½
11.35	415	–	–	–	–	970	1
11.40	335	230	20	55	38	880	2
11.50	250	220	20	55	65	690	2

An intermediate superheater was then fitted, which added some 100°F to the low-pressure steam and reduced the smokebox temperature. On 13 and 14 February test runs were undertaken with the dynamometer car from Darlington to London (Kings Cross) and back, from Darlington to Leeds and back on 21 February and from Edinburgh to Perth and back on 23 February. On its arrival at Edinburgh on 22 February the staff at Haymarket depot were told not to let out the fire in view of the difficulty of lighting-up when cold the next day.

In April some more tests were run to Leeds, and on 31 July it hauled the up Flying Scotsman from Edinburgh to London. After a few runs on this turn, including a failure on one of the up runs before reaching Newcastle, it was transferred to less important trains. Its high coal consumption probably made it too risky for long runs on the main line. Some reports put the coal consumption as high as 165 lb/mile, but this may have been only over a short distance at high output.

In this boiler design there was a brick-lined partition across the lower half between the inner and outer low-level water drums so that the air supply to the firegrate had to be fed between an inner and the an outer skin covering the water tubes. There was also a brick lining surrounding the firebox, but the lagging over this deteriorated and considerable difficulty was experienced in distortions of the boiler walls leading to air by-passing the firebox and so reducing the flue gas temperature. This also resulted in shortage of air for combustion and thus excessive fuel consumption. The preheating effect of the air passing over the boiler skin should have been beneficial, but it was the inability to keep this skin intact that was the major cause of the weakness of this type of boiler when applied to locomotive duty.

During the summer of 1930 the locomotive was based on Gateshead shed and it worked trains between York and Edinburgh, covering up to 420 miles a day. On one occasion the rear trailing wheels became jammed in a crossover and the 'Galloping Sausage', as it was nicknamed, had to be freed by a couple of 0–8–0 freight locomotives.

Other operational problems included leakage of high-pressure steam from the high-pressure steam chest to the intermediate receiver, as well as the erratic working of the reducing valve. These features probably prejudiced the adoption of compounding for the streamlined A4 Pacifics then being designed, but the work done on the front end design of No 10000 helped towards the front end design of the A4s.

The boiler tubes themselves presented no problem in spite of 1,536 expansion joints into the various drums. The feed water heated to over 400°F and led into the top drum was so effective that the period between boiler wash-out was four or five times that on conventional types.

During February and March 1931 regular running took place between Newcastle and York, including more dynamometer car tests, and after some further modifications the tests were resumed in July and August. On 4 September some special tractive effort tests were carried out at Shildon, but there does not seem to be any record of the results. The designed starting tractive effort was estimated to have been 32,000lb.

On 19 and 20 November indicator tests were taken between Darlington and York, and on one of these the driver managed to break the train in three places when the Flying Scotsman was only 20 minutes away – some handy signal wire enabled the train to be put together and out of the way just in time!

Further indicator tests were undertaken in February 1932 between Newcastle and Carlisle, followed by fuel consumption tests between Newcastle and Edinburgh combined with some measurements of flue gas temperatures in October and November, but there does not seem to have been any recorded running between these tests, so presumably a lot of time was spent at works.

Then according to Mr K. Hoole a 70,000-mile general repair took place in May 1933 after which there is no recorded running until some further tests took place in August 1934 with locomotive No 761 acting as a counter-pressure brake. These results do not seem to be available, but they must have been unsatisfactory because the front end was promptly redesigned to accomodate a double blastpipe and in March the order was issued to carry out this conversion.

High-pressure water-tube boiler in the works of Yarrow & Co., Ltd., Glasgow

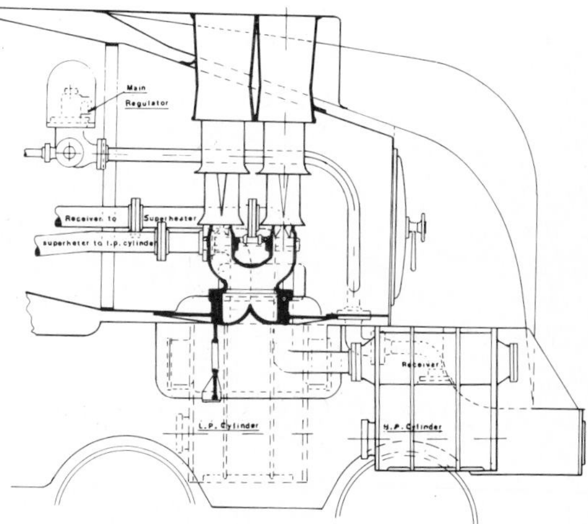

LNER 10000 double blast pipe arrangement

This work was completed on 10 May 1935 and the locomotive was displayed at an exhibition of rolling stock at Leeds on 11 and 12 May. Then based at Neville Hill depot, Leeds, it worked service trains to Newcastle for a week or so, and after some further modifications commenced a series of tests with the dynamometer car and No 761 as a counter-pressure brake between Leeds and Hull; these tests are fully recorded.

The new twin blastpipes were each 4.75in diameter in place of the 4.25in of the original single pipe. The new pipes could be fitted with four wedge-shaped bars and four sets of different sizes of bar were used in these trials. The total area of the new blastpipes was 35.4 sq ins and the fitting of the various bars reduced this area to:

No 1 set 16.9sq in equivalent to 4.65in dia
No 2 set 18.9sq in equivalent to 4.9in dia
No 3 set 21.8sq in equivalent to 5.3in dia
No 4 set 24.0sq in equivalent to 5.5in dia

The measurements taken in the tests that were run in May and June 1935 were as follows:

1 Back pressure in branch pipe from right-hand and low-pressure cylinder.
2 Exhaust steam temperature measured by resistance pyrometer.
3 Steam temperature from low-pressure cylinder measured by resistance pyrometer.
4 Steam temperature from low-pressure superheater by resistance pyrometer.
5 Receiver temperature read by thermocouple.
6 High-pressure superheater read by thermocouple.
7 Smokebox vacuum by pitot tube 10in behind rear blastpipe and 6in below the orifice.

All instruments were calibrated before and after the tests. The load consisted of the dynamometer car and locomotive No 761 set at 50 percent cut-off.

The only recordings currently available give results for Nos 1 and 3 bars, but not for Nos 2 and 4, so presumably these were not as good, if they were ever taken.

Back pressure readings, lb/sq in, were initially:

Drawbar hp	*No 1 Bar lb/sq in*	*No 3 Bar lb/sq in*
600	3.0	1.1
800	4.2	1.6
1000	6.0	2.0
1200	7.4	2.8
1400	–	3.8
1600	–	5.8

(Above) A head-end view of No 10000 showing the rectangular air intake combustion air which passed between the outer and inner skins covering the boiler tubes. *L&GRP*

(Right) Broadside view of No 10000, from a commercial postcard by The Photochrome Co.

Readings taken at various cut-off rates were:

	Cut-off *hp* %	*Cut-off* *lp* %	*Boiler pressure* *lb/sq in*	*HP* lb/sq in	*Smokebox vacuum* *in*	*Steam temperatures °F* *hp*	*Steam temperatures °F* *lp*	*Steam temperatures °F* *exhaust*	*HP power*
No 1 bars	30	35	470	395	1.5	645	470	220	220
	30	45	450	400	2.5	645	460	232	300
	40	35	460	400	5.7	650	530	234	975
	50	45	475	380	12.8	700	570	299	1,470
No 3 bars	30	35	430	380	2.2	560	400	220	580
	30	45	460	400	1.2	605	400	216	480
	40	35	460	395	2.0	620	430	219	930
	50	40	475	365	8.5	735	560	305	1,560

The final set of results taken on 6 June with the No 3 set of bars give basically similar results with a maximum output of 1,702 drawbar horsepower, a vacuum of 9in and an exhaust temperature of 299°F. The drawbar pull was just 5 tons at 57mph.

The cylinder efficiency according to these results should have been 22.6 percent at the peak output, thus thoroughly justifying the design of the cylinder motion and the double blastpipe, but it was unfortunately let down by the boiler performance which must have been below 50 percent. This never seems to have been properly measured, which again was unfortunate since it was the combination of good boiler design coupled with a similar cylinder layout that was the basis of the very successful fleet of Chapelon compound locomotives in France a few years later.

On 14 June 1935 a further visit to Darlington for the fitting of a cowl to improve the smoke drift caused by the soft exhaust from the double blastpipe resulted in another month of operation at Leeds until 21 August 1935, when No 10000 re-entered its birthplace for the last time.

Just over a year later on 13 October 1936 it was rebuilt at Doncaster with the standard A4 Pacific type of boiler with the streamlined front end and motion fairings, but still as a 4–6–4.

Its total mileage in $5\frac{1}{2}$ years of operation was quoted as just over 90,000 or 16,400 miles per annum. Allowing for two years of its life in shops, its operational figure was still only 25,000 miles a year. It was eventually numbered 60700 in the BR system and finally withdrawn in 1959. The main frame could have reached the million mile mark by the end of its rebuilt life.

The Yarrow boiler was later used in the Stooperdale shop at Darlington for supplying test steam until 1966, but its reputation was not of the best.

CHAPTER SIX

THE LMS *FURY*

The 'Race to the North', representing the rivalry between the East and West Coast routes from London to Edinburgh and Glasgow, had been dormant since the West Coast won in 1895, but after the effects of World War I and the amalgamation exercise in 1923, there were signs of this rivalry breaking out again.

Following the improvements to the Gresley Pacifics as a result of the Interchange Trials with the Great Western Castle class locomotives in 1925, the fuel consumption had been brought down to around 40 lb mile with a 400-ton train, so that a daily non-stop 393-mile run in each direction on the LNER between Kings Cross and Edinburgh (Princes Street) for the Flying Scotsman was commenced on 1 May 1928.

By way of a ripost on 27 April the LMS had run two trains non-stop from London (Euston), one to Edinburgh (400 miles) and the other to Glasgow (401 miles), but these were not daily service runs. Though it was shown that the LMS Royal Scots could do the 400-mile run, there was not sufficient margin to institute a regular service. A nominal non-stop service was later brought in, but with a halt just outside Carlisle Station to change locomotives.

In the search for a more efficient motive power unit which would be economic enough to run the 400 miles on one tender-full of coal, the LMS decided to try a high-pressure boiler fitted on one of the Royal Scot type 4–6–0 locomotives as built by the North British Locomotive Company, Glasgow.

The leading exponent of high-pressure steam production was the Schmidt superheater firm of Berlin, and it had produced some very high pressure boilers, (1,400 lb/sq in on locomotives for trials in Germany and in France). The German firm of Bauart had also just built a locomotive, No H 02 1001, with a Swiss Loeffler boiler at 1,800 lb/sq in (122 atmospheres).

Schmidt's representative in Great Britain, the Superheater Company, supplied and fitted the high-pressure portion of the boiler, while the low-pressure portion of the boiler at 250 lb/sq in was supplied by the North British Locomotive Company. The cylinders, pistons and valves were supplied by the LMS.

In December 1929 No 6399 *Fury* was handed-over to the LMS after 14 days' testing at the North British works, just a week after No 10000 had been completed by the LNER, thus putting the

(*Left*) The high-pressure unit in the boiler of No 6399 *Fury*. *Mitchell Library*

(*Right*) LMS high-pressure 4–6–0 No 6399 *Fury* outside the North British Locomotive Company's Hyde Park, Glasgow, works, on delivery in December 1929. *Mitchell Library*

East Coast in the lead in this race to try out higher than normal boiler pressures.

The Schmidt system as used on *Fury* consisted of three steam circuits; first a completely closed super-pressure circuit comprising the firebox walls operating at between 1,400 lb sq in and 1,800 lb/sq in; this supplied heat to the high-pressure steam drum from which separate steam fed the high-pressure cylinder at 900 lb/sq in. The exhaust from this high pressure cylinder was delivered to a receiver where it mixed with superheated steam at 250 lb/sq in from the low-pressure portion of the boiler.

The super-pressure circuit was filled with distilled water in order to avoid tube deposits, but there does not seem to have been any method of topping-up this circuit when in operation, though there must have been some pressure release system for safety reasons, and therefore some loss of water. This may have been the cause of the initial failure as the other similar units working in France and Germany were reported to have suffered from the same troubles.

The low-pressure (250 lb/sq in) boiler was supplied with water by both live steam and exhaust steam injectors; from this boiler water was fed to the high-pressure (900 lb/sq in) circuit by two Knorr-Bremse high-pressure pumps. Excess steam from the high-pressure drum was passed back to the low-pressure boiler drum.

The low-pressure boiler constructed by the North British Locomotive Company was of nickel steel, as was the 900 lb/sq in drum, which was a machined forging supplied by John Brown & Co of Sheffield. The supplier of the super-pressure tubes is not mentioned, but these appear to have been made from a steel with a carbon content of 0.1 percent. These tubes were 2in (50mm) external diameter with a nominal thickness of 0.156in (4mm).

Following a period of crew training, the locomotive steamed from the North British Hyde Park works to Polmadie shed on 6 February 1930. During that run the right-hand pump discharge chamber fractured.

On 10 February the fire was lighted at 7.0am and the locomotive was ready to run by 10.30am. Leaving Polmadie at 10.35am with driver Donald Hall and fireman Donald Blair, Francis Pepper of the LMS from Derby, and Lewis Schofield of the Superheater Company on board, it ran to Hamilton Palace Colliery South Box, seven miles from Polmadie, at around 30mph. There the driver

Low-pressure and high-pressure units in position on the boiler of *Fury*. *Mitchell Library*

called the attention of Mr Schofield to the water level gauge of the closed circuit, then down to 3in, but was told that this was satisfactory.

On slowing for an adverse signal in Carstairs station, the fire suddenly blew out of the firebox door, but the driver was able to put on the brake before a hasty departure from the cab. When the engine stopped he was able to return and put out the fire. The fireman escaped with a few broken bones by jumping on to the station platform, and the LMS representative was badly scalded on the legs. Mr Schofield of the Superheater Company was in the centre of the cab and was so badly burned that he died on his way to hospital.

According to the driver's evidence at the subsequent inquiry, the steam pressure in the three circuits had not exceeded 1,100, 800 and 200 lb/sq in respectively during the run, and apart from the water level previously mentioned there was no sign of any trouble. A relief locomotive towed *Fury* dead to Polmadie where it was examined, and an opening some 5in long found in one of the super-pressure tubes above the top of the firebox.

Following the official inquiry on 21 March the problem was remitted to Professor F. C. Lea of the University of Sheffiield, and his report was issued on 28 May. From samples of tube near the failure it showed that distortion had taken place with a corresponding reduction in wall thickness by 0.03in and an increase in the Brinell hardness number from 118 to 140. This indicated that the critical temperature of 800°C had been reached, which was almost certainly caused by a dry pocket or insufficient flow of steam. There was a slight seam groove in the tube at this point and this was so minute that it was not considered to be the root cause, but a failure would tend to follow this groove, which in fact it had.

It was probably due to having to call in outside expert advice that caused the LMS shortly

The burst high-pressure tube, found on examination after the failure on 10 February 1930. *Scottish Record Office*

afterwards to set up its own research department which has grown into the establishment at Derby to-day. After a lot of correspondence between Derby, the North British Locomotive Company and The Superheater Company, the boiler was rebuilt at the NBL works and No 6399 was towed to Derby for some further trials.

All this seems to have taken some two years, since the first recorded run was a dynamometer car test on 10 July 1932, when a run was made from Derby to Trent Junction with a train of 308 tons. The combustion was poor, with plenty of black smoke, but that is not surprising since the crew had been instructed to keep the firehole door shut as much as possible, though even this precaution would not have been proof against any further blowout at 1,400 lb/sq in.

The distance run was 37.5 miles covered in 77 minutes with a maximum speed of 45mph. The average work rate was 204hp with a coal consumption of 33lb/mile, equivalent to 0.07 lb/ton-mile. There is no record of any steam pressure or temperatures being read at any of the critical points in the system, nor of any cylinder outputs. Perhaps it was intended to take these on the next trial on 25 September 1932. On that occasion two return runs were made from Derby to Trent with 350 tons. The combustion was slightly better with the firehole door kept open, but the coal consumption was slightly worse at 47.2 lb/mile.

The final run as *Fury* was on 14 February 1933 when the locomotive set out from Derby for

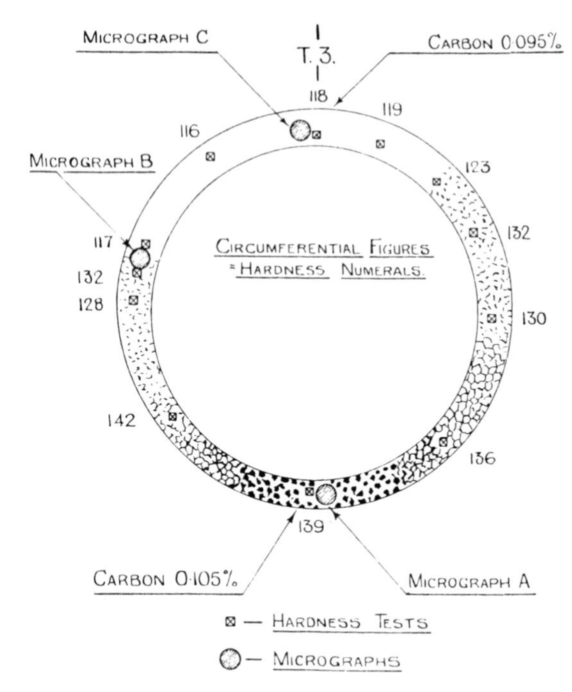

Analytical diagram of the failure of the high-pressure water tube (serial no 2011).

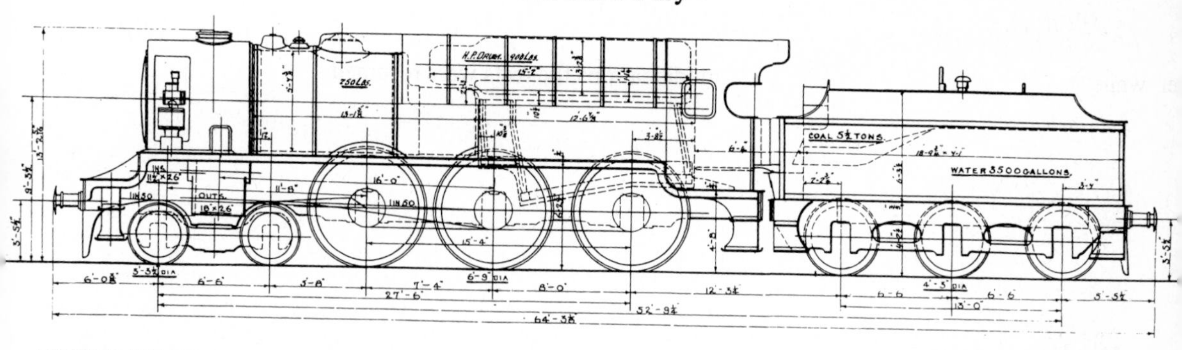

(*Top*) General diagram of No 6399.

(*Above*) *Fury* rebuilt as the forerunner of the rebuilt Royal Scot 4–6–0s, No 6170 *British Legion*.
British Railways LMR

Wellingborough with the dynamometer car and 54 freight wagons, just over 1,000 tons. The steaming was fine as far as Trent, but then pressures began to fall and by Syston Junction a load of clinker had to be removed from the firebars. Towards Oakham the pressure in the high-pressure drum kept falling to 500 lb/sq in and eventually a pilot locomotive had to be attached. Then near Kettering a coupling broke on the seventh wagon and the pilot had to be detached to fetch in the rear half of the train. *Fury* worked alone towards Wellingborough with the dynamometer car and the first few wagons, but failure of the feed pumps caused the fire to be drawn and the locomotive was finally towed to its destination and then back to Derby.

There it was rebuilt as No 6170 *British Legion*, the forerunner of the converted Royal Scots when they were rebuilt with taper boiler and redesigned cylinders. *Fury* must have travelled more miles under tow than under its own steam and can only have been a financial liability to all concerned.

The West Coast route definitely lost out in this portion of the 'Race to the North'.

CHAPTER SEVEN

THE LMS TURBOMOTIVE

In 1932 the German State Railway, in the depths of its depression, surprised the railway world by producing a high-speed diesel-electric railcar set called *Flying Hamburger* which ran from Berlin to Hamburg at a speed of 77mph. In that year also the Great Western succeeded in running its Cheltenham Flyer from Swindon to Paddington at an average speed of 81.7mph.

These events seem to have awoken the slumbering northern giants, who then both took $8\frac{1}{4}$ hours to get to Scotland. Whether by accident or intent, the LMS produced its first Pacific locomotive No 6200 *The Princess Royal* from Crewe works in 1933. This was to revive the old 'Race to the North' between the East and West Coast routes to Scotland, at that time the cream of the railway traffic.

It had been intended to produce three of these Pacifics initially at Crewe, but in the previous year William Stanier, the LMS chief mechanical engineer, had been persuaded by Dr Guy of Metropolitan-Vickers to pay a visit to Sweden in order to study the working of the latest Ljungström turbine locomotive, a 2–8–0 then operating on the Grangesberg to Oxelosung line with 1,500-tonne freight trains. This locomotive which was non-condensing had a boiler pressure of 185 lb/sq in with a steam temperature of 752°F, a turbine output of 1,270hp at 27mph and a maximum speed of 43mph. A tractive effort of 47,040 lb was claimed as against 38,000 lb for an equivalent piston type locomotive with an adhesive weight of 72 tons. This gives a factor of adhesion of 29 percent, rather on the high side, but obtainable possibly by reason of the smoother torque from the turbine.

The trials with this turbine unit had shown savings of 7.26 percent in coal and 15 percent in water, and on this basis it was decided that the third of the LMS Pacifics should be built on this principle. This was a brave venture in view of the failure of the earlier Beyer-Ljungström locomotive, but the weak points in the former design such as the condenser and the air pre-heater were eliminated and the remainder of the locomotive was similar to the Princess Royal class. The steam temperature was raised from 750°F to 850°F, but the overall heating surface

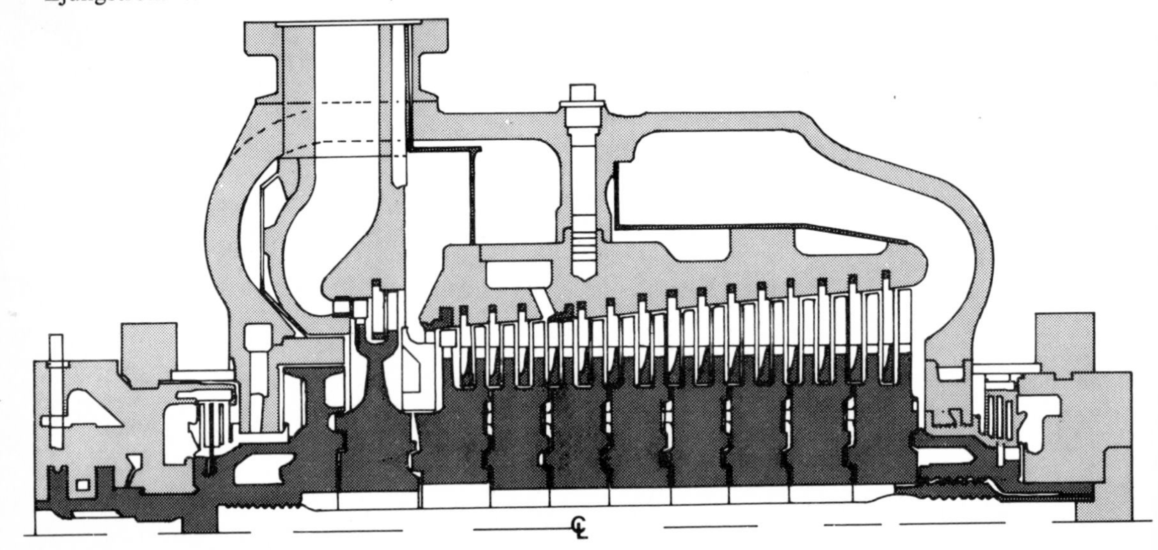

LMS TURBOMOTIVE Nº 6202
Half section of main turbine

General right-hand side view of Turbomotive No 6202, showing the reverse turbine.

area was 2,168sq ft compared to 2,516sq ft for Nos 6200/1.

The elimination of hammer-blow allowed the axle load on the driving axles to be increased from 22.5 tons to 23.6 tons, thus giving 69 tons adhesion against 67.5 tons for Nos 6200/1.

With a boiler pressure of 250 lb/sq in, the starting tractive effort was estiminated to be 40,000 lb for both piston and turbine types, but it was estimated that the elimination of fluctuating forces and of piston back pressure would show economies of 6 percent in fuel and water for the latter.

The Princess Royal class was fitted with four cylinders 16$\frac{1}{4}$in diameter by 28in stroke, and with 6ft 6in driving wheels. The turbine for No 6202 had an output at rail of 2,400hp at 7,060rpm corresponding to 62mph, and the tractive effort at 70mph was intended to be 12,000lb (5.36 tons) against 9,000 lb for the standard Pacifics, a considerable increase since Churchward's proposed 2-ton pull at 70mph in 1902.

The main turbine built by Metropolitan-Vickers (who it was said had claimed to make the best turbines in the world, and 'if anybody wanted one they could bloody well come and ask for it!') had 18 rows of blades and was controlled by six admission valves; the maximum back-pressure at exhaust was designed to be 2 lb/sq in, and in order to obtain sufficient draught for combustion, a double blastpipe was fitted.

The drive to the front driving axle was through a triple-reduction gear having a ratio of 33 to 1, and the gearing was enclosed in an oil-tight casing. The gearing originally had been intended as a double-reduction unit, but this had to be redesigned after some tests on the turbine, which meant higher working speeds on the turbine itself.

Three oil pumps were provided, one driven off the gear train, and two steam-driven to supply cooling oil when at rest at a pressure of 7 lb/sq in. The gear-driven pump boosted the oil pressure to 16 lb/sq in at 60mph and an oil cooler was designed to keep the maximum oil temperature down to 180°F.

A feed water heater was supplied with steam bled from the turbine at the sixth stage. All the axles were fitted with Timken roller bearings.

A turbine has one serious disadvantage for rail traction applications in that it will only run in one direction and either a reversing gear has to be fitted, or a separate reverse turbine. On No 6202 the latter was chosen and a reverse turbine with four rows of blades was fitted. This was normally disengaged, but could be brought in by means of a dog clutch when the locomotive was stationary; when the reverse turbine was in use the main turbine was not disengaged.

Although turbine locomotives were not intended for service operation in reverse, and normally only ran light engine in that condition, there were times when main line locomotives had to work empty stock out of Euston to the carriage sidings at Wembley, and it was found that the reverse turbine was inadequate for this purpose.

One other disadvantage of a turbine is that the continuous exhaust loses the lifting effect on the

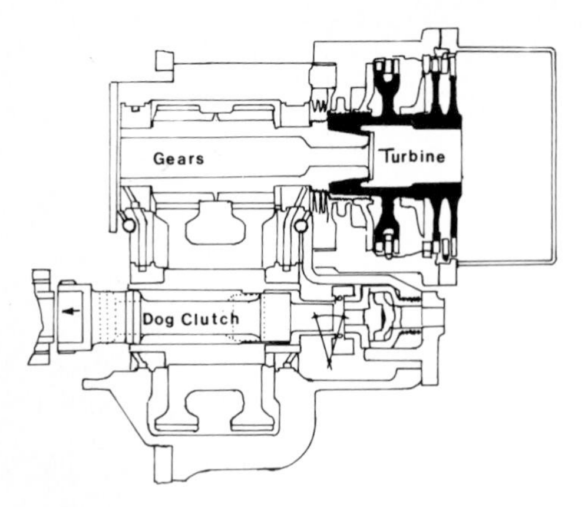

LMS No 6202 reverse turbine

firebox obtained by the piston pulsations, particularly when working hard, and this can vitally affect the boiler output. Initially the steaming was reported as poor, but this was improved by disconnecting the variable blastpipe gear and setting this in the minimum position.

The first two LMS Pacifics Nos 6200/1 had been named *The Princess Royal* and *Princess Elizabeth*, but No 6202 carried no name initially though it was unofficially christened 'Turbomotive'. It was put into service in June 1935 and operated between London (Euston) and Liverpool (Lime Street) running 395 miles per day. This route was later selected for two diesel-electric prototypes, the original *Deltic* and for DP2.

Due to the soft exhaust it was found necessary to fit smoke-deflector plates in order to keep the cab vision clear, while a speedometer had to be fitted owing to the difficulty in detecting wheelslip. Speedometers had never been popular in the UK, and drivers always reckoned that they could tell their speed by the exhaust beats, but the Flaman recorder had always been accepted in France and even welcomed as it provided a basis for bonus payments to the footplate staff.

After two months' operation and 6,100 miles, the leakage of oil from the turbine bearings and the presence of water in some of the roller bearing axle boxes, led to a modification of the oil seals and entailed 26 days' work lost.

In September after a further 3,000 miles, and

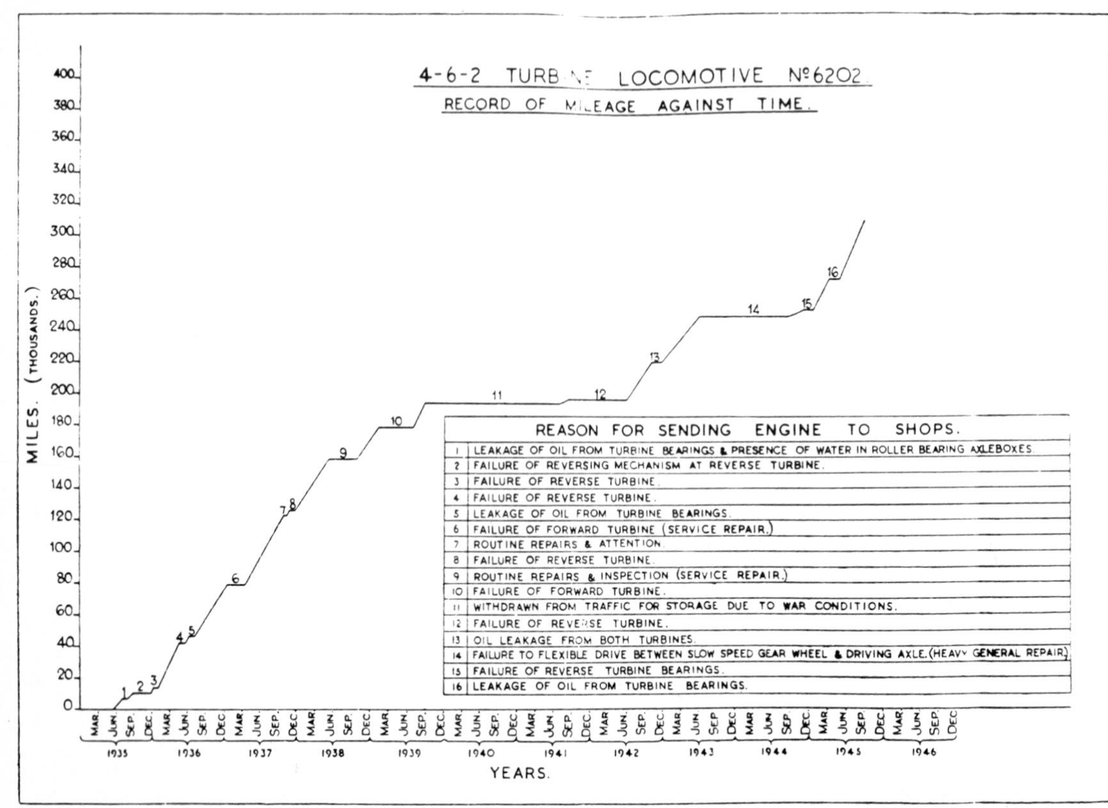

Record of Mileage Against Time.

No 6202 in Crewe Works in the late 1930s. This view shows the brackets to support the casing over the main turbine on the left-hand side of the locomotive. *W. H. Whitworth/Rail Archive Stephenson*

when at Liverpool, the two halves of the reverse turbine clutch failed to engage, but steam was applied, and the clutch teeth were badly damaged. This meant a complete overhaul of the turbine and reversing gear with the loss of 76 working days. In January 1936 when at Euston after 12,644 miles, a similar event to that at Liverpool took place. Following this incident an inching gear was fitted so as to ensure the engagement of the dogs before steam admission. This cost 17 operating days.

In May the first of three sets of dynamometer car trials was carried out on the Royal Scot between London (Euston) and Glasgow in comparison with the latest of the second batch of Princess Royal Pacifics, No 6212. These test results will be analysed later, but they did show that the Turbomotive was slightly better in performance and coal consumption. No 6202 completed its tests on 7 May.

On 15 May after 40,653 miles, the white metal bearings in the main turbine ran when at Cambden shed causing the rotor to foul the stationary blades. Both turbines were overhauled, but no reason was found for this fault. Thirty-four working days were lost on this occasion.

Two months later at 45,688 miles oil leakage was found to be due to emulsification; the oil reservoir only held a one-minute supply of oil, compared to at least five minutes for stationary turbines. The drain pipes were inadequate for oil flow when frothing, and oil overflowed from cavities surrounding the turbine bearings. A larger oil sump was fitted and at the same time a new boiler with a 40-element superheater was installed. This only took 15 days, extremely good for the amount of work involved.

In October 1936 the second set of dynamometer trials took place with the new boiler installed. These runs from the 26–28 October involved the Royal Scot, the down 2.00pm once known as 'the Corridor' and the up night mail and sleeper. The comparable locomotive on this occasion was No 6210 and this time there was little to choose between them.

When shunting at Willesden in January 1937 after 78,812 miles, the main turbine rotor seized due to the movement of a stator diaphragm. A radial movement of $\frac{1}{8}$in caused blade contact, stripping one row of blades. Key collars were then fitted to lock the diaphragms in their slots. This

A glimpse of No 6202 in service on the up Merseyside Express, at Brinklow, Staffs, on 30 September 1937. *T. G. Hepburn/Rail Archive Stephenson*

time the tyres were turned and a sludge removal cover was fitted to the oil tank. This work took 64 days.

The third set of dynamometer car trials took place in June 1937, all on Royal Scot runs, with slightly better results. On one run the coal consumption was below 40 lb/mile with 489-ton train.

Routine repairs and turning of tender tyres took place in October followed by a further failure of the reverse turbine in November, losing 36 working days in all.

In June 1938 at 158,500 miles a complete service repair was undertaken. This involved the overhaul of both turbines, all tyres turned, 40 boiler tubes changed and 523 steel stay nuts changed. The time out for all this was 123 days.

The next failure was the only one in operation at speed, as the main turbine spindle fractured when running at 60mph on an up train near Leighton Buzzard, fortunately without damage to train or track. This meant a complete rebuild of the turbine and lost a further 147 days of useful work.

From August 1939 No 6202 was withdrawn from traffic due to pressure of war work at Crewe and at Metropolitan-Vickers. It remained out of service for nearly two years until it was restored to traffic in July 1941. Two months later at 195,370 miles the reverse turbine failed again due to oil shortage and an additional Worthington pump was fitted to augment this oil supply. The reverse turbine again had to be rebuilt, and due to delays at Metropolitan-Vickers this failure cost 257 days lost work.

A further case of oil leakage from both turbines caused 42 days delay in November 1942, and in January 1943 the driving wheels locked when at Camden shed. This was due to the flexible drive between the final gear and the driving axle. Wear in the driving pins had caused contact between the nuts and the gear-wheel disc, causing the nuts to work loose. Ten teeth on the pinion were broken-off and 68 plates had fractured in the 16 spring drives. As the total mileage was then 249,300, a general overhaul was carried out including wheels, boiler, turbines and gears. This took 378 days.

Just 3,200 miles after return to service the reverse turbine failed again, due to cotton waste from the previous repair obstructing the oilways, and in April 1945 a further case of oil frothing caused loss of oil and another larger oil sump was fitted.

No 6202 ran on in its original form for another four years when the increasing problems of obtaining turbine spares led to its being rebuilt in as a Princess Royal class Pacific. It was then named *Princess Anne* and as such was finally written-off after being involved in the disastrous accident at Harrow on 8 October 1952.

An analysis of the dynamometer car results shows that this locomotive was little different from the other Princess Royal class Pacifics, and apart from the time spent in shops for turbine repairs, it was operationally quite successful. No 6202 did show a noticeable improvement over the other Pacifics in its uphill times, but this may have been due to its control system in that the choice between one valve opening and the next is a coarser control than that obtainable with the cut-off selection on the normal piston valve gear. A good driver would select the cut-off so as to maintain the schedule time with the minimum steam and coal

Table 6
Dynamometer Car Results for LMS Turbomotive No 6202

FIRST TRIALS, MAY 1936
Euston – Glasgow, 402 miles

Locomotive No	*Speeds (mph)*		*Train weight (tons) to*			*Dbhp*	*Coal consumption*		*Water*
	average	*maximum*	*Crewe*	*Symington*	*Glasgow*	*average*	*lb/mile*	*lb dbhp/hr*	*gallons/mile*
6202	53.70	80.00	564	470	304	787	42.00	2.85	31.50
6212	52.50	80.00	569	507	337	770	45.00	3.10	38.00

Glasgow – Euston, 402 miles

Locomotive No	*Speeds (mph)*		*Train weights (tons) to*			*Dbhp*	*Coal consumption*		*Water*
	average	*maximum*	*Symington*	*Crewe*	*Euston*	*average*	*lb/mile*	*lb dbhp/hr*	*gallons/mile*
6202	53.70	75.00	327	–	497	706	40.50	3.10	34.00
6212	53.70	77.00	305	–	472	655	40.00	3.30	34.00

SECOND TRIALS, OCTOBER 1936
Euston – Glasgow, 402 miles

Locomotive No	*Speeds (mph)*		*Train weight (tons) to*			*Dbhp*	*Coal consumption*		*Water*
	average	*maximum*	*Crewe*	*Symington*	*Glasgow*	*average*	*lb/mile*	*lb dbhp/hr*	*gallons/mile*
6202	53.20	85.00	454	–	486	943	49.60	2.80	38.50
6210	–	–	480	512	496	841	46.80	2.90	38.90

Glasgow – Euston, 402 miles

Locomotive No	*Speeds (mph)*		*Train weight (tons) to*			*Dbhp*	*Coal consumption*		*Water*
	average	*maximum*	*Symington*	*Crewe*	*Euston*	*average*	*lb/mile*	*lb dbhp/hr*	*gallons/mile*
6202	50.00	78.00	–	495	519	755	50.00	3.30	38.80
6210	49.00	81.00	–	534	560	678	44.00	3.20	36.00

THIRD TRIALS, JUNE 1937
Euston – Glasgow, 402 miles

Locomotive No	*Speeds (mph)*		*Train weight (tons) to*			*Dbhp*	*Coal consumption*		*Water*
	average	*maximum*	*Crewe*	*Symington*	*Glasgow*	*average*	*lb/mile*	*lb dbhp/hr*	*gallons/mile*
6202	55.30	85.00	–	489	320	858	42.40	2.73	38.00

Glasgow – Euston, 402 miles

Locomotive No	*Speeds (mph)*		*Train weight (tons) to*			*Dbhp*	*Coal consumption*		*Water*
	average	*maximum*	*Symington*	*Crewe*	*Euston*	*average*	*lb/mile*	*lb dbhp/hr*	*gallons/mile*
6202	55.70	81.00	–	–	483	826	40.20	2.71	36.00

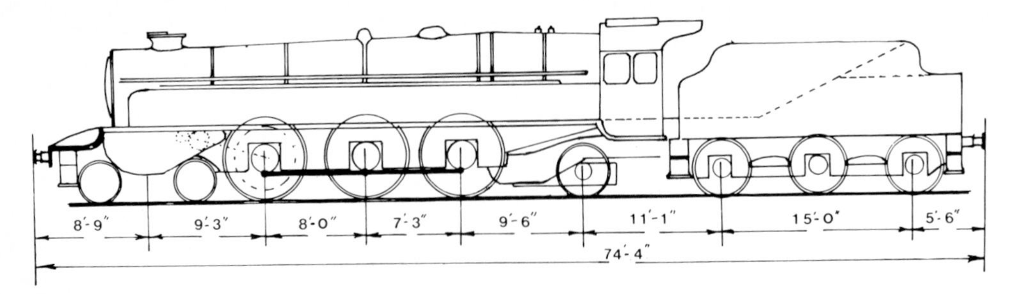

LMS No 6202 outline diagram

consumption; no doubt to-day a modern traction type governor could be applied to a turbine to give this fine control, but such was not available at that time.

No 6202 made no spectacular runs such as those of the 16/17 November 1936 when No 6201 *Princess Elizabeth* ran the 401 miles to Glasgow in 353 minutes, and back in 344 minutes, though with only 260 tons of train. Those runs were in anticipation of the Coronation Scot which commenced service in 1937 and nearly wrecked itself on the invitation run for the Press and guests in attaining 114mph momentarily on the approach to Crewe. This speed was later to be eclipsed by the 126mph of LNER A4 Pacific No 4468 *Mallard* next year on the East Coast route, but at least the Coronation Scot was unique in having an expressive theme tune written for it.

As the last of the pre-war steam prototypes No 6202 was thermally a success story, but the delays due to spares and unusual operating problems precluded any further trials of this type of locomotive in the UK. Its average annual mileage was only 28,500 compared to 53,000 for the Princess Royal class and 73,000 for the later streamlined Coronation class, though No 6202 did achieve 66,200 miles in 1936.

The fuel saving achieved was more than offset by the loss of mileage and the extra cost of maintenance. The Turbomotive represents the last of the steam experiments in trying to improve efficiency by non-standard methods. The only post-war attempts at novelty include the disastrous Southern Railway Leader locomotive discussed in the next chapter, and the Franco-Crosti boilers on the BR Class 9F 2–10–0, which was a sound idea badly applied.

While we in the UK were worrying about obtaining 400mile runs on 8 tons of coal, this must be contrasted with the last days of steam operation on the New York Central Railroad where it was trying to work 1,500-ton express trains over the 960 miles from Harmon to Chicago without a change of locomotive. Using a tender weighing 188 tons and carrying 46 tons of coal this still entailed one coal replenishment stop giving a consumption of 0.12 lb/ton-mile. In order to achieve this result, water pick-up troughs were used, but with a tender water capacity of 18,000 gallons this would need to be refilled at least ten times on a run of that length.

Table 7
Best uphill timings with 480-ton train

			Minutes taken by locomotives Nos			
Section of line	*Miles*	*Sched. (mins.)*	*6202*	*6210/ 6212*	*6201*	*71000*
Euston–Tring	32	38	37.1	38.7	29.9	31.7
Stafford–Whitmore	14	16	13.8	14.9	11.9	12.5
Oxenholme–Shap	19	26	22.1	22.9	16.5	24.3
Beattock–Summit	10	18	15.2	18.3	9.5	–
Symington–Beattock	17	18	16.3	23.2	13.7	–
Carlisle–Plumpton	13	20	18.5	20	12.4	–
Penrith–Shap	13	19	15.1	19.6	12.5	–
Crewe–Whitmore	10	14	13.2	14.6	9.6	–
Bletchley–Tring	15	16	12.5	14.6	11.3	–

Notes:
1. No 6201 16 and 17 November 1936 runs were with 260 tons
2. Figures for No 71000 are from BR Test Report No 15

CHAPTER EIGHT

THE BULLEID LEADERS – SOUTHERN RAILWAY AND CÓRAS IOMPAIR EIREANN

In the chapter on the Paget locomotive it was mentioned that it might have been dubbed 'Bulleid Beware'. It would have been interesting to know how much of the troubles relating to the Paget were disseminated as far as Doncaster where Bulleid was trained, since so many of the Paget features were included in the design of the Leader.

O.V.S. Bulleid (although he preferred Pugh as a Christian name to that of Snell) went to the Southern Railway in 1937 but he very soon made a profound impact there, starting with his Pacific No 21C1 *Channel Packet*, introduced in February 1941. Though designed to weigh $92\frac{1}{2}$ tons this locomotive came out nearly seven tons overweight and had to be lightened to bring it finally to 94.8 tons. His next design of a lighter Pacific which came out in 1945, was designed to 86 tons and weighed correct to design.

These two classes which both had chain-driven valve gear and thermic syphons, were excellent at producing steam, but erratic in operation. In prime condition drivers considered them the best locomotives available, but they were not as reliable as the Lord Nelson 4–6–0s, and their overhaul mileage worked out at 36,000 compared to that of 48,000 for the Nelsons.

In 1944 the Southern Railway general manager asked for ideas for the building programme for 1946, which included 25 passenger tank engines to undertake fairly arduous duties as replacements for some ageing tanks of varying vintages, and designs were put forward for 0–6–2, 0–6–4, and even some 4–6–4 tanks.

Bulleid wanted to ensure the maximum adhesion to compare with the Southern's Co-Co electric locomotives, and submitted a design to diagram W7169, based on a C–C wheel arrangement to be driven by six cylinders 12 3/8in by 14in, operating at 280 lb/sq in boiler pressure and weighing 100 tons.

During the design and development various sizes of cylinders were considered and the final dimensions were $12\frac{1}{4}$ by 15in. In order to accomodate three cylinders in each bogie it was found necessary to adopt a form of sleeve valve with reciprocating and rotational motion with a uniflow steam system. This design to diagram W7326 had a central cab. Five locomotives were ordered to that plan, but the design was later amended in diagram W7457 to allow a separate driving cab at each end.

The basic specification for the locomotive was

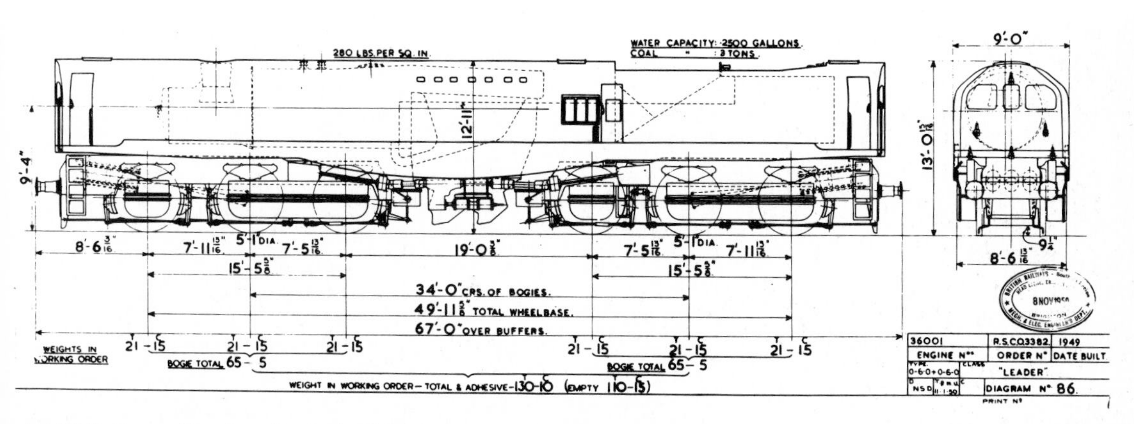

British Railways (Southern Region) official general diagram of No 36001

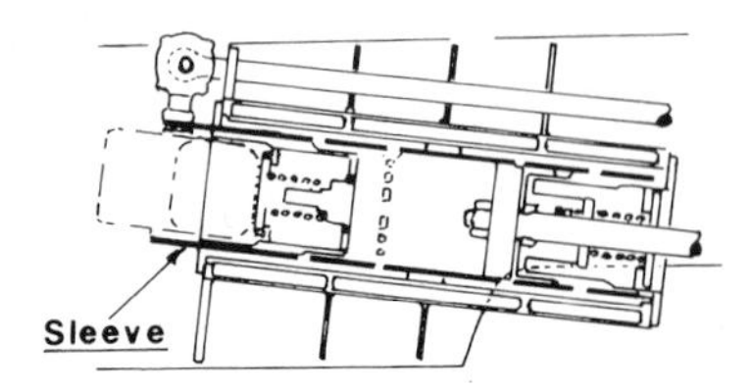

"LEADER" CYLINDER and SLEEVE VALVE

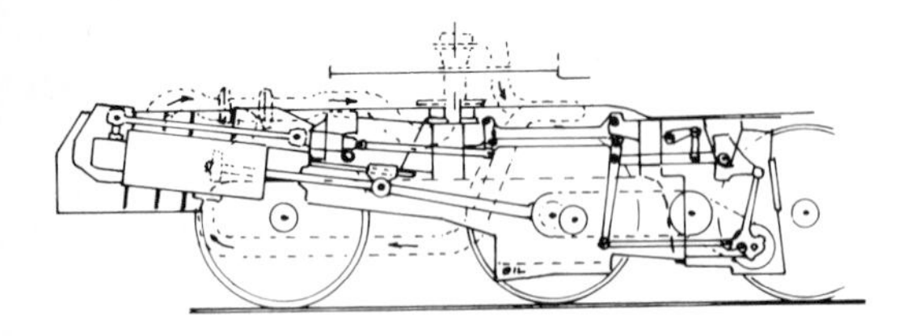

SOUTHERN "LEADER" No 36001

BOGIE LAYOUT

Detail drawings of the cylinder and sleeve valve and bogie layout of No 36001.

to include the following features:

1 To be able to run over the majority of the Company's lines.
2 To work all classes of train at up to 90mph.
3 To have the whole weight available for braking and adhesion.
4 To run with good visibility in both directions.
5 To be ready at short notice.
6 To be continuously available.
7 To be suitable for common-user work.
8 To run at least 100,000 miles between general overhauls.
9 To impose the minimum wear on the track.
10 To use less fuel and water per drawbar horsepower (dbhp).

Out of these ten items only numbers 3 and 4 were achieved.

The final design included two 6-wheel bogies with 5ft 1in wheels in which the centre axle was to be driven by a 3-cylinder sleeve valve engine, and from which the outer axles were actuated by a chain drive. Owing to space limitations only one axle could be driven off each end of the driving axle, which entailed a thrust in opposite directions from each end of the driving axle. The axle-boxes were fitted with tapered roller bearings and moved vertically on cylindrical pedestals, to eliminate side play.

The boiler was to produce steam at 280 lb/sq in, using a firebox with brick walls and a steel crown plate into which four thermic syphons were welded; the boiler barrel was also to be welded. In order to permit through passage between the cabs

No 36001's boiler, showing the thermic syphons.

View of one of the 3-cylinder power bogie units.

and to the firing area, the boiler had to be mounted off-centre. Finally, the TIA (Traitement Intégrale Armand) system of water treatment was adopted, which metered supplies of additive to keep the feed water alkaline.

The material for the first five Leaders was ordered by December 1946 and manufacture started at Brighton in July 1947. At that time it was decided to try out the cylinder and valve gear on a former LBSCR Class H1 Atlantic No 2039 *Hartland Point*. The locomotive was modified by 3 December 1947, and in the presence of H. G. Ivatt of the LMS carried out a yard trial in which it was enveloped in a cloud of steam, just as the Paget had been.

During 1948 No 2039 *Hartland Point* ran a series of tests between Lancing and Eastleigh, and in order to reduce the steam leakage, the sleeve valves eventually were fitted with 36 sealing rings. These were subject to breakages as was the actuating mechanism, but at least there were no seizures as on the Paget. On test the water consumption was high, as much as 70 gallons/mile, which would entail a coal consumption of over 60lb/mile – not a promising start.

Unfortunately there was not time for any further development work on *Hartland Point* as the first set of Leader frames was ready at the Brighton Works in May 1948. There was a tendency for the cylinder blocks to warp after welding to the frames, but the first complete bogie steamed sweetly on test until the engine was accidentally reversed, causing buckling of the rods and links.

By June 1949 No 36001 was complete, and steaming trials commenced with runs over the line from Brighton to Uckfield and Crowborough. On one occasion a run was started with the intention of reaching Victoria, but this was sharply vetoed by order from Marylebone, and so No 36001 was never seen in London.

No 36001 was 67ft overall and came out considerably overweight at 131 tons instead of the 112½ tons intended. The weight included in the diagram was three tons of coal and 2,500 gallons of water, although alternative figures have been quoted as four tons and 4,000 gallons. The tractive effort was 26,300 lb, compared with 24,600 lb

No 36001 nearing completion at Brighton Works, May 1949. *National Railway Museum*

Prototype Leader Class No 36001 on one of its dynamometer car trials in September 1950. *L. Elsey*

for an LMS 2–6–4T, and 30,000 lb for the SR Q1 class.

The locomotive was most unpopular with the firemen, who had to endure a stokehold temperature of up to 120°F. There had been an intention to name the class, with the first two suggested as *Missenden* (then the BTC Chairman) and *Churchill*, but this was not to be. Some of the names suggested in the works such as *Fred Carno* were much less flattering.

By the end of 1949 just over 5,000 miles had been run with 20 failures, mostly with the valve gear, and with spalling of the firebox brickwork. At this time the locomotive was returned to Brighton for modifications which included doubling the sleeve valve clearance, removing the oscillating gear from the sleeve mechanism and removing the rocking grate feature. Since the weight was greater on one side by some 10 tons due to the offset boiler, this was redressed by ballasting, but this only increased the overall weight. The driving chains were lengthened to avoid stretch which had upset the timing, and the firebox lining had to be increased in thickness, which reduced the grate area from 43sq ft to only 26sq ft and affected the subsequent steaming abilities. The valve drive mechanism which was enclosed in an oil-tight frame as in the earlier Pacifics, suffered from the presence of water in the oil due to condensation, giving a tendency to prime, but there was not time to cure these faults on this occasion.

No 36001 re-entered service in June 1950 based at Eastleigh, and after a further 860 miles suffered a fractured crank axle. This may have been due to torsional vibration, though with a rotational speed of 272rpm at 60mph this seems improbable. However the power take-off at each end of the axle was in opposite directions, so the internal strains must have been considerable.

In September 1950 some tests were conducted using the LNER dynamometer car between Eastleigh and Woking with trains of up to 325 tons, but the results were very disappointing. The boiler pressure averaged 240 lb/sq in with a high exhaust pressure of 7.30 lb/sq in. The inlet steam temperature was 550°F with the exhaust at 285°F, so it is not surprising to find the overall effiiciency at only 2.82 percent. Coal consumption averaged 50.2 lb/mile or 6.7 lb/dbhp and the water consumption was 38 gallons/mile. These figures compared with 30 lb coal/mile and 25.4 gallons of water used by SR U Class 2–6–0 No 31630 on the same duties, an efficiency of 4.7 percent.

Finally, after the dynamometer car had been returned to the LNER, No 36001 made a swansong run on 2 November 1950 with a 480-ton train (its designed load) from Eastleigh to Basingstoke (26 miles) in 46 minutes which included a 1½-minute signal stop, but that was its last known run and it was then withdrawn.

In March 1950 a report by Ron Jarvis, Mechanical Engineer (Design), condemned various aspects of its design including the weight, the lubrication system, the firebox and the valve gear. It also mentioned that the fireman's space was dangerous and liable to blow-back in tunnels.

As a back-up, a memorandum from HQ stated that the cost by then had come to £176,000 for the five being built, as against an estimate of £100,000, and compared that with costs for a Class 5 4–6–0 at £16,000, a 1,600hp diesel-electric at £78,000 and a Co-Co electric at £37,000. Following the results of the dynamometer car trials there was no case to continue with this project and it was finally abandoned in March 1951, the locomotive having by then only run a total of 7,117 miles.

In 1949 Bulleid went to the CIE (Córas Iompair Éireann) at Inchicore, Dublin and revived the idea of the Leader as a turf-burning project. The idea of using turf had been investigated by John Aspinall in 1885, who doubted its commercial value since turf had 2½ times the bulk of coal and 50 percent of its calorific value. However Bulleid persuaded CIE to embark on this trial in which he wisely enlisted the aid of Bord na Mona. In Eire little could be achieved without its approval at that time.

The first stage was an experimental rig built at Inchicore based on a 1903 Great Southern &

Western Railway 2–6–0 No 356, modified to burn turf with a mechanical feed and a forced-draught fan driven by a steam turbine, which used most of the steam produced. This fan was replaced by a diesel-driven fan, but a forced-draught fan was found unacceptable and the design changed to use an induced-draught fan. This had to handle the hot gases, but the temperature was reduced by means of a heat exchanger which was used to dry the turf and to extract some of its 25 percent moisture content. No 356 did eventually manage a run as far as Cork, and in 1953, despite a general swing towards diesel locomotives, sanction was given for 50 steam locomotives to be fired by oil or turf.

Eventually the design of this Leader was finalised as a C–C intended to produce 1,000hp with a capacity for 12tons of turf (occupying 1,200cu/ft) and 3,000 gallons of water. This locomotive was to have a welded boiler with two barrels 4ft by 4ft 8in by 8ft each side of a central firebox 6ft long. The boiler design included 720 small tubes, since there was little risk of fouling with such a clean fuel. The cab was to be central and at each end of the locomotive was a 50hp steam-driven fan which drew the exhaust from each smokebox through the water space. The turf was fed from its hopper by a feed screw into a chamber below the cab floor and then by another screw to the firebox.

Bearing in mind the problems with the other Leader, the first intention was to use a 6-cylinder flat Ricardo poppet valve steam engine in each bogie driving through a Mekydro gearbox to three Mekydro final drive units, one on each axle, but this scheme was ruled out on cost, and the final design was based on a 2-cylinder engine with cylinders 12in by 14in, with 7in piston valves driven from a shaft mounted below the cylinder block. The wheel diameter had been intended as 4ft, but owing to problems in obtaining wheels of that size a diameter of 3ft 7in was chosen.

The whole project met with the usual dilatory approach of the Emerald Isle so familiar to those in the former LMSR who had dealings with that country. Eventually Bulleid enlisted the help of J. G. Click and A. R. Pocklington of the Rugby Test Plant who went to Inchicore in March 1956. They first tried to redesign the locomotive as a much simpler single-ended job, but were too late with this idea; numbered CC1 the locomotive was completed in June 1957 as originally designed, with steaming trials on 23 July. On 9 August it was visited by Monsieur Armand of the SNCF who rode in the cab, and its first outing was to Sallins on the 13 August followed by trials with 11 bogies on 15 and 21 August. On 4 September it ran to Kildare with 160 tons followed on the 5th with 225 tons and on the 6th with 255 tons; on the latter run the consumption of turf was 99 lb/mile. On 25 September it ran light engine to Cork, followed by the same run on 1 October with 165 tons, reaching up to 70mph. Its final run was accompanied by H. G. Ivatt and R. C. Bond as far as Straffen, when it put in a final spurt at 65mph. It was inspected by parties from the Institution of Locomotive Engineers in May 1958, and from the Institute of Transport in June, when it performed very satisfactorily on both occasions.

This machine seems to have been much sounder mechanically than its former Southern version and in its short life achieved some 2,000 miles of trouble-free operation, though it is doubtful if it ever achieved anything like the 1,000hp intended.

The main complaint was that the grate area was too small, with resultant spark throwing, but that could probably have been overcome. It was however too late to arrest the general changeover to diesel power in Ireland, both north and south of the Border, but it did show what could be achieved by faith and persistence.

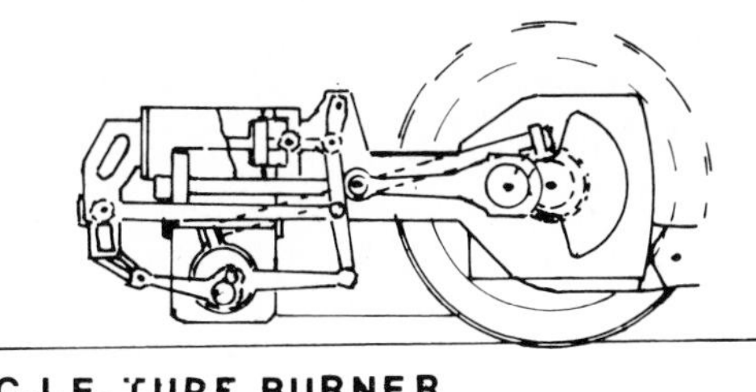

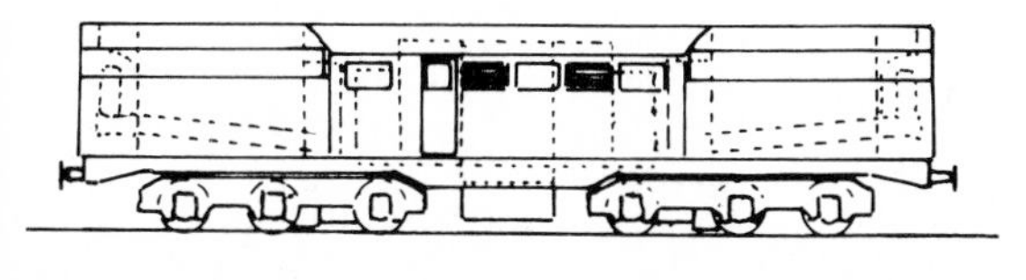

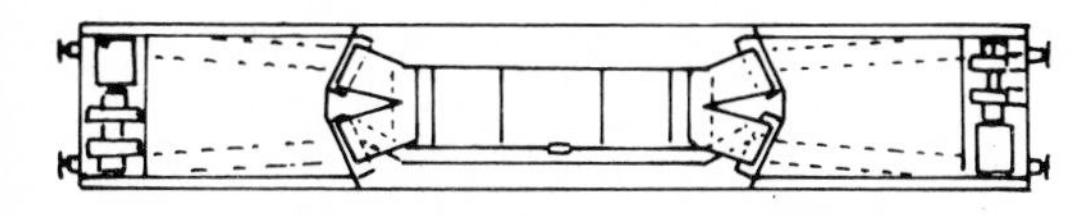

General layout and details of the valve gear on the CIE turf-burner No CC1

CHAPTER NINE

The Second No 10000

When the second No 10000, a 1,600hp diesel-electric, was built by the LMS at Derby it was a real race against time as the chief mechanical engineer, H. G. Ivatt was determined to produce it as an LMS locomotive before nationalisation, which took effect on 1 January 1948. This was achieved with a month to spare, but it was touch and go. The whole project had been agreed between H. G. Ivatt and Sir George Nelson of the English Electric Co Ltd in May 1946, and it was completed, at the expense of a lot of steam locomotive work at Derby works, by the end of November 1947.

The LNER and the Southern Railway had also been considering the use of 1,600hp main line diesel locomotives but the LNER scheme had been too ambitious, embracing 25 locomotives, and that had foundered on post-war financial stringencies. The Southern had been schizophrenic between wholesale electrification and partial diesel operation, and no firm decision had been reached before the end of 1947.

No 10000 was based on the then current American expertise in diesel locomotives, but conditions there were so vastly different with a much more generous loading gauge (about 12in extra in both height and width) and with permissible axle loads up to 28 tons, that they had no problem in putting their largest main line diesel engine (the General Motors EMD567 16-cylinder at 1,500hp) on a Bo-Bo or an A1A–A1A. In No 10000 a heavier power unit was put on to a Co-Co wheel arrangement with an axle load of just over 21 tons, a remarkable feat of pioneering design work by E. A. Langridge.

Three other pioneer features were tried and tested in No 10000: the diesel engine itself, the first application of the new English Electric uprated 10in by 12in engine in VEE form; the control system, including a new traction type engine governor; the novel 3-axle twin bolster bogies designed by Edward Fox. Problems there were, but on the whole all three features were amazingly successful, particularly the bogies.

The English Electric Company had entered the rail traction market in 1927 when it had produced the electrical equipment for a 500hp railcar set built by the LMS, using the Beardmore airship diesel engine as fitted in the R101. This had proved disastrous since the engine was structurally weak, and the whole set was underpowered. In 1934 English Electric produced its own 10in bore diesel engine called the K model. The 6-cylinder version, the 6KT, became the standard engine for the LMS 350hp shunters. This engine earned itself a good reputation for reliability, and could run for up to 40,000 hours between major overhauls.

During the 1939/45 war the Royal Navy wanted more powerful diesel engines, and the K engine was fitted with a turbocharger, redesigned as both in-line and VEE form layouts, and uprated to 100hp per cylinder at 750rpm. A 2-cylinder unit VEE engine was built for test and development, as well as a 12-cylinder engine to test the turbocharging system. The results were sufficiently satisfactory for the engines to be offered for rail traction applications. The Royal Navy wanted the engine to be built with a

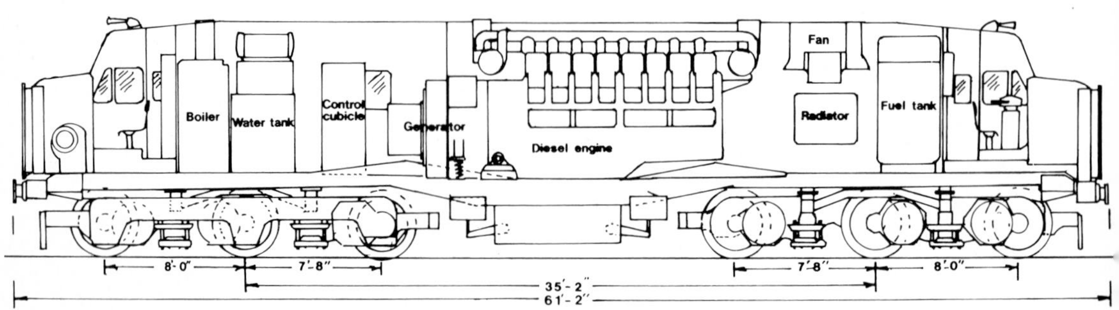

LMS Nº 10000, 1600 HP DIESEL ELECTRIC LOCOMOTIVE GENERAL ARRANGEMENT

A bogie frame being assembled at Derby for No 10001. *British Rail*

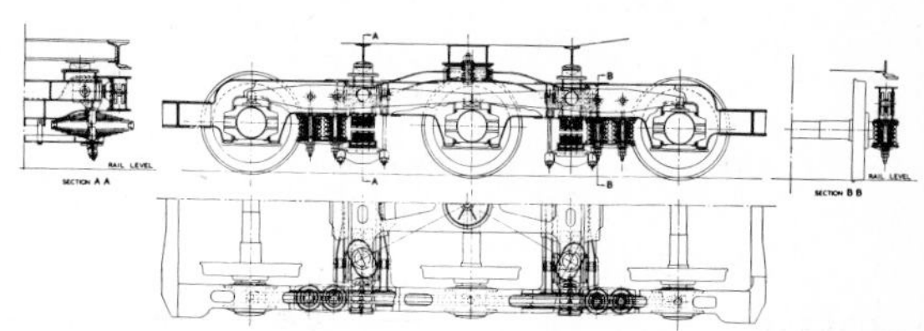

Diagramatic arrangement of bogies.

fabricated crankcase to withstand mine detonations, but English Electric wisely decided to retain castings for bedplate and crankcase, which were cast in its Rugby Works, in a special Mehanite formula.

The first railway contract for the RK engine, as it was called, was for the Egyptian State Railway and included 49 four-cylinder engines for railcars, and 13 of the 16-cylinder version for main line locomotives. It was one of the latter that was fitted in No 10000, but due to problems in the development of the 16-cylinder version, the 16SVT the engine was not delivered to Derby until May 1947.

Since there was insufficient headroom in the erection shop at Derby to lower the power unit through the roof of the locomotive, the bodysides had to be removable and could not act as stress-bearers. This meant that the main frame had to be constructed of deep rolled-section joists which took a lot of finding at that time of post-war shortages; cutting and welding had to be kept away from any stressed portions of the frame. The power unit was located centrally between the two bogies, with the radiator and fuel tanks at the free end of the engine, and with the control cubicle and train heating boiler at the generator end (Fig 22). A lot of testing was carried out in co-operation with Spanner Ltd to see if an exhaust gas boiler was feasible, but it would have been impossible to accomodate it and the heat available would have been insufficient at part loads.

The bogies were box structures of welded plate with brakes on both sides of all the wheels, and a slack adjuster on the main pull rod. The original design had been based on an A1A type using two motors, and a design with eight wheels had even been considered, but when English Electric decided that three motors were necessary, the design had to be changed; this involved the use of an arched H member resting on two bolsters between the axles which carried the main bogie centre frame in an oil bath. The equaliser beams carrying the weight to the axles were located within the box forming the main frame giving these bogies a very clean appearance.

The brake cylinders and battery box were located between the bogies and the American pattern of nose end was adopted to safeguard the driver from sleeper flutter, though the Southern Railway with its experience on multiple-unit stock had shown this to be an unnecessary waste of space. The nose end was of greater significance in the United States in protecting the cab crews from the results of their frequent level crossing accidents with highway vehicles, and it tended to improve the otherwise box-like appearance of the flat-fronted body. The nose contained only a compressor and a traction motor blower with

No 10001 under construction at Derby showing the massive frame construction. The picture shows the boiler fuel and water tanks, control cubicle, diesel engine radiator, fan ducting, and fuel tanks. *British Rail*

passage space for a corridor connection; this feature was of little value and was a nuisance through being a source of draughts in the driving cabs.

To design all this within an overall length of 61ft 2in was a remarkable feat, since all subsequent main line diesel-electrics of this power output were longer than this. Even the 2,000hp Warship diesel-hydraulics were only 1ft shorter and they were on a B–B wheel arrangement – the Deltics and the Class 40 locomotives were 69ft 6in. The overall weight was intended to be 120 tons but came out finally as 130.6 tons with a maximum axle load of 22.2 tons. This was less than a Duchess Pacific, but it did limit availability despite the absence of hammer-blow effect.

No 10000 was driven out of the Derby shop on 8 December 1947 by H. G. Ivatt. Unfortunately it would not move at first as H.G. did not realise that a brake application had to be made to ensure the closing of the safety contacts before power could be applied. It then went to Euston for a press demonstration, travelling via Market Harborough and Northampton, and commeneed service operation with a run from Derby on the 10.47am to London (St Pancras) on 14 January 1948 with a 393 ton train.

Operation continued between St Pancras, Derby, and Manchester (Central) until July 1948 when the second locomotive, No 10001, came into service. No 10000 then went to Derby for inspection, having run 51,300 miles in six months. In October both went to Camden shed and commenced multiple operation between Euston and Carlisle on 4 October until 10 October when No 10000 failed and had to be returned to Derby. If either one was out of action the other was transferred to Derby for operation on the former Midland main line, in spite of their high axle load.

The most troublesome equipment was the oil-fired train-heating boiler, which was the first to be tried out in the UK. The relays and pumps were not suited to the conditions found in a main line locomotive with vertical and transverse stresses as high as 2g; these units could not be relied on for passenger train operation in the winter months and the locomotives were put on to freight working between Camden and Crewe during that period.

During their winter operation on freight work some measurements were taken of fuel consumption, and over 3,965 hours this came out as 123,943 gallons for 136,439 miles. The fuel per ton mile worked out at 0.015 lb – (85 watt hours per ton mile).

In May 1949 No 10000 and 10001 were back on multiple main line working, and one of H. G. Ivatt's favourite cab tales was of a horn malfunction when running north from Tring on the Royal Scot, which should have meant stopping at Leighton Buzzard as a failure. He told the driver to go flat out through the single line tunnel at Linslade (just beyond Leighton Buzzard), and that cured the horn problem. That was the only spot on the line where that could have been effective.

As an engine testbed No 10000 was very effective and engine faults soon showed up. One of the first and worst of these was oil emission from the cylinder head and crankcase covers. A dirty engine does not encourage good maintenance and tends to get neglected. Fuel injection equipment, timing chains and turbochargers also gave troubles of varying sorts, calling for changes in design, but many of the desired changes could not be incorporated in the Mk 1 engines in Nos 10000/1.

The control gear was also novel and small faults in relays and contacts could soon cause on-line failures. The control system on Nos 10000/1 had eight notches on the driver's controller giving step speed control at only three engine speeds, 450rpm, 600rpm and 750rpm, with torque control in notch 8 only. This meant a big variation in engine output according to the notch selected, the maximum drawbar horsepower available in the various notches being: 3 200hp, 4 250hp, 5 350hp, 6 450hp, 7 800hp, 8 1,320hp. The record on the Camden to Crewe freight service indicates an almost continuous use of notch 8 for that run.

In February 1953 Nos 10000/1 were transferred to the Southern Region to work in conjunction with that Region's first two diesel-electric units Nos 10201/2. They first had major overhauls at Brighton works as each had run nearly 400,000 miles. The opportunity was taken to alter the big-end bearings from white metal to copper lead, to conform to the type fitted in the later engines supplied to the Southern Region.

The locomotives worked main line trains to Bournemouth, Salisbury and Exeter until 1955 when they returned to the London Midland Region. Based on Willesden shed, they worked the Anglo-Scottish trains in multiple, but working singly they were mostly used on freight between Camden and Crewe. Individually they were little better in performance than a Jubilee or a Black Five though noticeably better uphill. The Brown

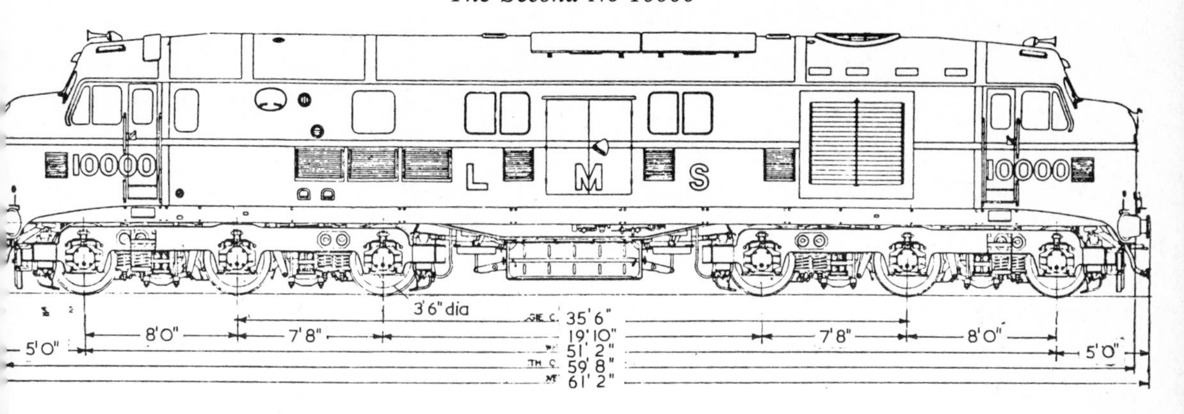

Nos 10001 and 10000 working in multiple on the up Royal Scot, passing Camden Goods Depot in 1951. *Rail Archive Stephenson*

No 10001 in solo use on the Southern Region. Note the early 'lion-and-wheel' emblem on the side. *W. Philip Conolly*

Boveri turbochargers suffered from high exhaust temperatures, often nearly 1000°F due to the inability to keep the correct fuel pump tappet adjustments.

In 1956 both locomotives spent nearly a year in Derby Works, largely due to poor supply of spares. It was unfortunate for English Electric that the MkI engines were out of production at that time, as the spares situation prejudiced the attitude towards the company's engines just as the dieselisation programme was being launched.

While these locomotives were at Willesden a system of spectographic analysis of the lubricating oil was initiated and this saved some serious troubles with the bearings by detecting high levels of copper in the oil.

When main line diesels built under the modernisation plan began to appear in strength on the London Midland Region in 1959, Nos 10000/1 were relegated to local and freight trains in the North London area, and after further visits to Derby in 1962 were virtually withdrawn. No 10001 returned to Willesden in December 1965, kept alive by cannibalising No 10000, and was used to work freight trains to Hither Green on the Southern Region, pending the arrival of the Class 33 1,550hp Bo-Bos. It remained at Willesden until 1967 and was scrapped from there by Cox & Danks at Acton, after running just over one million miles.

No 10001 was the only prototype diesel locomotive to achieve this mileage in its original form, No 10000 making around 850,000 miles. No 10000 really deserved a place of honour at the York Railway Museum, but preservation was not in the air in 1968. That turbulent year which saw the end of steam in the UK as well as riots in the USA, in France and in Ulster, also saw the end of No 10000 at the hands of J. Cashmore of Great Bridge, Staffordshire.

CHAPTER TEN

THE SOUTHERN TRIO – NOS 10201/2/3

The Southern Railway produced many modernisation schemes after 1945 including total electrification, partial electrification supplemented with diesels, and in the end the Southern Region at British Rail was the last to maintain main line steam working out of a London terminus, Waterloo, using its rebuilt Bulleid Pacifics.

As a result of these variations the Southern's decision to build main line diesel locomotives was well behind that of the LMS and its first locomotive, No 10201, did not emerge from Ashford until November 1950. The Southern Region having had plenty of experience with small-wheel multiple-unit motor bogies, imposed an axle load of 18 tons, in which it was ahead of the rest of BR. Knowing the overall equipment weight from No 10000, the bogie design included an extra pony axle, and being designed by Percy Bolland was very similar to those used on the Co-Co electric locomotives. The highest axle load actually came out at 18.5 tons in working order, with an all-up weight of 135 tons.

Diagram of bogie as used on SR diesel-electric 1Co-Co1 locomotives Nos 10201–3.

The power unit was the same 16-cylinder English Electric 16SVT engine as fitted in Nos 10000/1, but it was equipped with the company's own Napier TS100 turbochargers and carried a one-hour rating of 1,760hp. The fuel was gravity-fed with an engine-driven transfer pump, and the air to the engine was fed through bodyside-mounted Vokes dry filters. The cylinder heads were the Mk I two-valve type as used on No 10000, but the main and big-end bearings were copper/lead in the original palm-ended connecting rods. The cylinder heads had safety valves as called for in marine type engines, but this was not found to be necessary in rail traction applications and was later deleted.

The body of the locomotive was flat-fronted, as the Southern had found that the nose end was quite unnecessary. Like the LMS design, the side panels were detachable for engine removal.

The main generator was an EE823A rated at 1,155kW and the power unit was mounted on 3-point suspension. The radiator fan motor was electrically-driven and the external radiator shutters were thermostatically controlled. The six traction motors were of the English Electric

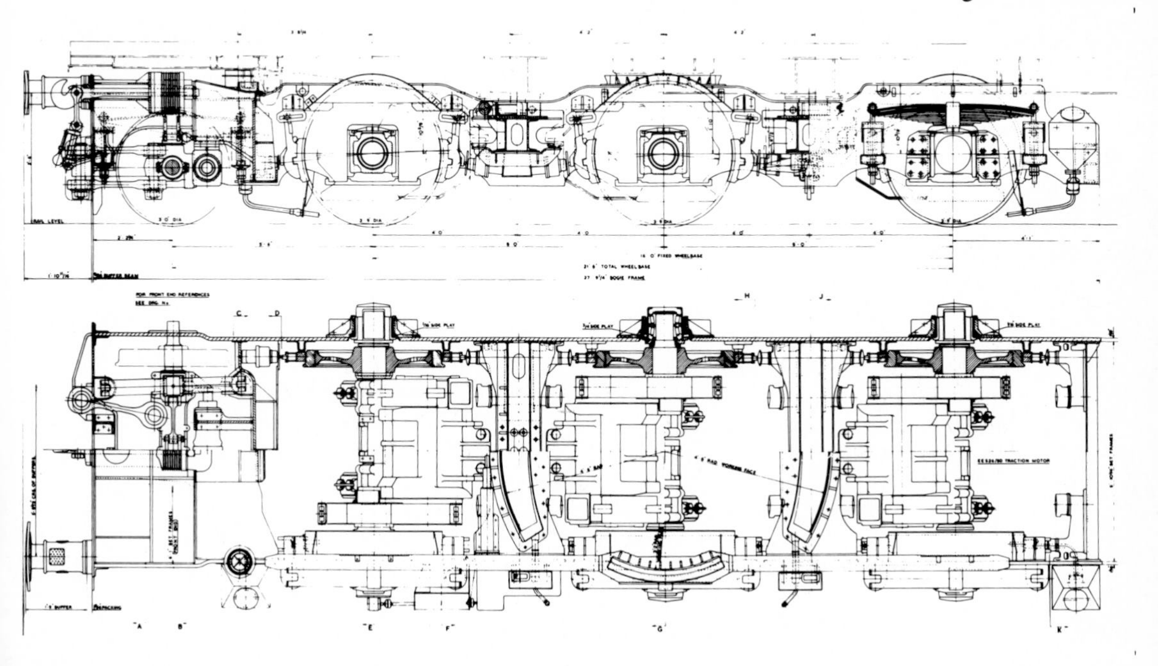

519/4D type, nose-suspended and forced-cooled with a gear ratio of 52/21 designed for a top speed of 110mph – this was intended as a prototype for high-speed services to Exeter and to Bournemouth. Twin compressors and exhausters were fitted as well as a Spanner Spiralflow oil-fired train heating boiler, with 880 gallons of water. The fuel tank capacity at 1,150 gallons was generous for the Southern system, since this would permit of three round trips from Waterloo to Exeter, and some weight could have been saved in this respect.

No 10201 ran a trial trip with 327 tons to Ramsgate in December 1950, returning to Ashford for painting and final adjustments. It ran light to Rye on 27 December, then to London (Victoria) and back on 28 and 29 December with a 260-ton passenger train.

On 4 January 1951 it was appropriated by the London Midland Region and transferred to Derby; there it was put to operate between London (St Pancras) and Manchester (Central) via the Peak Forest route, but the traction motor gearing was not designed to operate on steeply-graded lines and traction motor temperatures exceeded their limits. It was taken out of service on the 17 January, sent to Ashford for repainting and was then put on exhibition at the Festival of Britain site on the South Bank of the Thames on 5 February, from whence it was finally extracted on the 24 November, thus losing nearly a year's operation.

In January 1952 it went to Nine Elms depot and then to Eastleigh for driver training. In February it worked the 09.54 ex Waterloo, and locals to Bournemouth, Woking, and Exeter until 11 March when a traction motor failed at Templecombe. The Bournemouth Belle Pullman train was worked on Sunday 16 March and from then it ran on Weymouth workings until a bogie fire caused a return to Brighton Works on 5 June. It returned to the Weymouth line on 28 June and then alternated between that line and the Exeter route, when it was joined by the LMS pair Nos 10000/1 in February 1953. In one incident No 10201 ran away down the 1 in 37 gradient between Exeter Central and St David's, but the driver just had control by the time the latter station was reached. On 7 March another traction motor fault at Andover caused a return to Brighton for the rest of the month. Apart from troubles with the train heating boiler, the traction motor field coils were the most frequent cause of visits to Brighton works.

Before No 10201 was able to get away from the Festival site its sister No 10202 came out from Ashford in August 1951, and after some running to and from Ramsgate, started work between Waterloo and Exeter one week and Weymouth the next, putting up between 3,400 and 4,120 miles per week. On 15 October when due to work the 13.00 express from Waterloo, a banjo bolt on one of the turbochargers was found to be fractured and the run was completed with the English Electric service engineer sitting astride the hot main generator and feeding oil into the bearing reservoir; such was the ardour in those days to ensure successful operation.

On 24 October a special high-speed run was planned from Salisbury to Waterloo with the Civil Engineer's permission to go up to 100mph, but this was cancelled by the Railway Executive as a result of some connecting rod failures on its new Britannia class Pacifics. It was thought that a high-speed diesel run was not the sort of publicity desirable just then. The run was carried out with eight coaches instead of the five as originally proposed, and with a stop at Andover. The 83.8 miles were run in 84 minutes with an unofficial

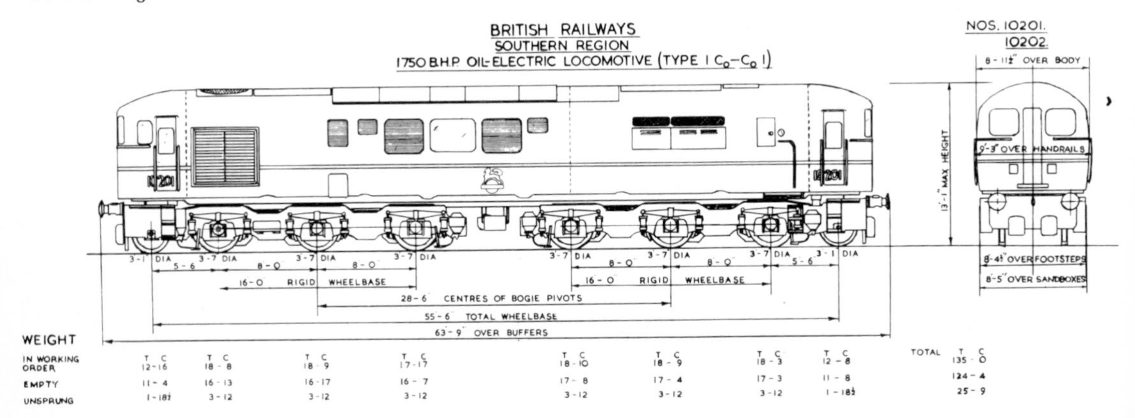

General weight and dimensions of No 10201.

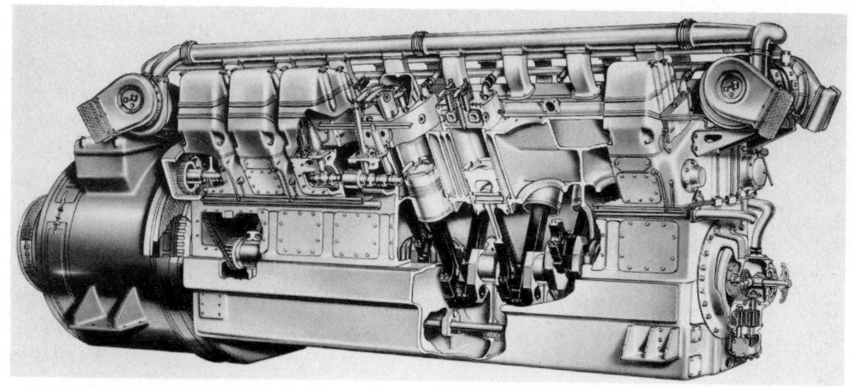

English Electric MkII 16SVT engine. *English Electric Co.*

maximum of 92mph near Hook.

Five days later No 10202 commenced a four-leg diagram with the 01.25 newspapers ex-Waterloo, returning on the 07.30 from Exeter, then the 13.00 from Waterloo to Exeter, followed by the 17.53 from Exeter, making 4,122 miles a week. The average fuel consumption worked out at 1.11 gallons/mile including train heating (estimated at eight percent of the total).

From 28 April 1952 No 10202 carried out four days of testing with the Swindon dynamometer car between Waterloo and Exeter with up to 432 tons trailing load; the mileage then was 89,270 and the original high-speed gear ratio was still fitted. These tests confirmed the operational findings already known, with a fuel consumption of 1.03 gallons/mile without train heating, and a drawbar efficiency of 18.63 percent. They also showed the desirability of altering the gear ratio, which was carried out at Brighton after 100,880 miles, when the diesel engine had an intermediate overhaul at 3,025 hours. The gear ratio was changed to 65/17 and an extra stage of field weakening added.

A further series of analytical tests were carried out in October 1952 for four days, by which time the mileage was 130,310. These showed that the effect of the gear change was to increase the tractive effort by 23 percent at 20mph, to reduce it by 10 percent at 70mph, and with no change between 35 and 50mph. The starting tractive effort was claimed as 48,000lb, but the best recorded was 37,820 lb according to the dynamometer car readings. These latter tests produced a whole lot of figures that were already known to the designers and operators of electric units, but the steam folk had to be convinced.

Just over a month later the camshaft drive chain broke, necessitating a visit to Brighton for 12 days. After this No 10202 returned to its normal roster, working from Nine Elms where it was joined by the LMS pair, giving four main line diesel diagrams on the West of England route out of Waterloo.

Cross-section of English Electric 16SVT engine, showing inclined bolt connecting rod, as originally fitted to No 10203.

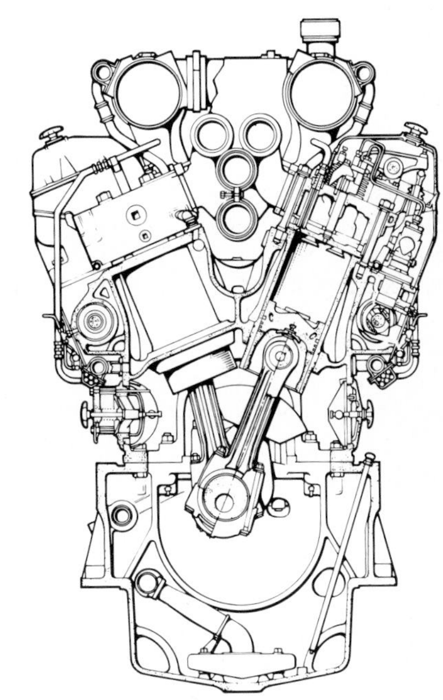

In March 1954 the Southern's third locomotive, No 10203, which had been built at Brighton came out, and was given the usual proving runs, this time between Brighton and Tunbridge Wells, a route not now possible. This locomotive was equipped with the new Mk II English Electric 16SVT engine uprated to 2,000hp, as later fitted in the Class 40 fleet. This engine had a 4-valve cylinder head and a redesigned connecting rod with inclined bolts, enabling it to run at 850rpm; it also had Napier

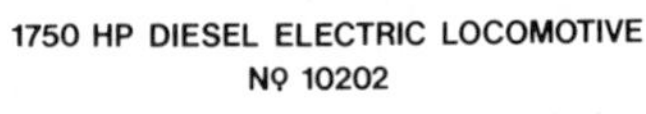

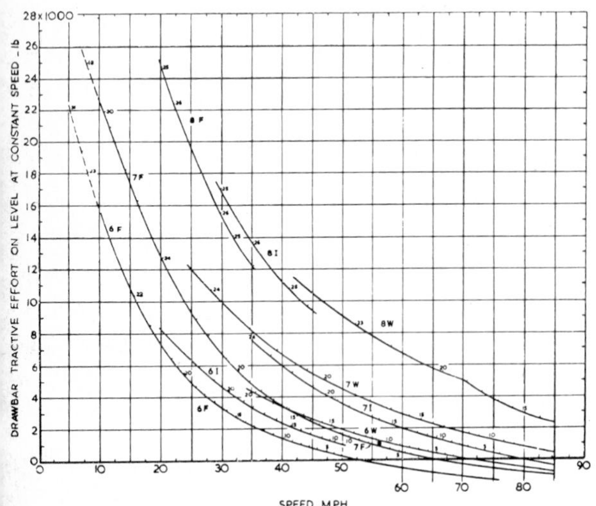

DRAWBAR TRACTIVE EFFORT CHARACTERISTICS WITH EFFICIENCIES

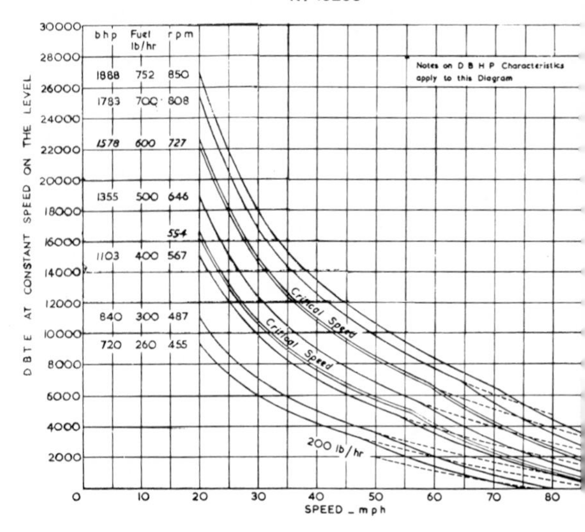

EQUIVALENT D B T E CHARACTERISTICS
(Drawbar T E at constant speed on the level)

MS100 turbochargers and thin-wall copper/lead bearings with a tin flashing for the big-ends.

The fuel feed to the injection pumps was pressurised instead of being gravity-fed as in the other four locomotives, and the crankcase breather was taken into the radiator fan, thus making for a much cleaner engine compartment. The cylinder head covers were redesigned, but still not really oil-tight, and bellows type expansion joints were used in the exhaust manifolds. Two major weaknesses of this engine, the chain driven camshaft and the bevel gear drive to the water and oil pumps, were unfortunately maintained, but the cost of changing these features could not be justified at that stage in view of the poor outlook in the rail traction market. These features were later eliminated in the Mk III version, but that was 15 years away.

The main generator was the English Electric 822/1B, and the six traction motors, type EE 526A, had a gear ratio of 19/61, with three stages of field weakening (55 percent, 37 percent and 25 percent), but the major improvement from the operating aspect was the pneumatic engine-speed control. This worked throughout the whole engine speed range from 450rpm to 850rpm (except for the critical speeds at 594rpm and 727rpm where the governor passed these speeds from 25rpm below to 25rpm above with continuous torque control).

After proving trials No 10203 went to Nine Elms in April 1954. From 25 May until 4 June it was shown at the International Railway Congress Exhibition at Willesden. It went into revenue-earning service on the Exeter line in July, was transferred to work the Golden Arrow (Victoria-Dover) for a week in March 1955, and in June/July carried out a series of dynamometer car trials after running 106,000 miles.

These took the form of controlled load test with train weights from 63 to 392 tons, and on service runs on semi-fast trains such as the 13.00 from Waterloo stopping at Woking, Andover, Salisbury, Templecombe, Sherborne and Yeovil, returning on the 17.55 from Exeter stopping at Sidmouth, Seaton Junction, Axminster, Yeovil, Templecombe, Salisbury, Basingstoke, Woking and Surbiton. The results were similar to those obtained earlier with No 10202, but the extra power of No 10203 was shown in its being able to take an extra coach (30 tons) and in spending less time under power (157 minutes against 182 minutes).

Other comparisons from these results gave fuel consumptions for No 10203 as 0.68 lb/dbhp hr, against 0.695 for No 10202, and the lb/ton-mile as 0.023 against 0.0248. One thing these tests did show, which should have been obvious to anyone studying their quoted performance, was that they were not up to the performance of the Southern's

No 10203 at Waterloo with the down Atlantic Coast Express.

Bulleid Pacifics as these comparable figures show:

Speed (mph)	*Tractive effort on level track – lb*		
	No 10202	*No 10203*	*MN**
20	25,000	26,800	–
30	17,000	18,000	19,000
40	11,000	13,500	15,000
50	9,000	10,500	12,000
60	7,000	8,500	10,000
70	5,000	6,600	8,000
80	3,000	4,500	6,000
90	–	2,000	–

*unrebuilt

Even uphill, some timed runs on the 1 in 80 gradient up towards Honiton gave the following speeds:

Locomotive No	10202	35022*
Train weight (tons)	286	290
Location	*Speed (mph)*	
MP 148½	25	26
MP 149½	30	37
MP 150½	30	41
MP 151½	31	45
MP 152½	31	48
MP 153½	40	50
Honiton	65	78

*unrebuilt Merchant Navy class

This shows what could be extracted by a skilled driver, from a steam locomotive in good condition, and the results confirmed the intention of the Southern Region to retain its modern steam fleet up to the electrification of the Bournemouth line in 1967. From these results the estimated run times for No 10203 on the Western Region, compared with a King class 4–6–0 on a 500-ton train worked out thus:

Section	*Minutes taken by*	
	No 10203	*King*
Paddington–Southall	13	12
Southall–Slough	8	8½
Slough–Reading	16	15½
Reading–Newbury	18	16
Newbury–Savernake	17½	16½
Savernake–Patney	9½	11
Patney–Castle Cary	28½	34
Castle Cary–Taunton	23	25½
Taunton–Whiteball	12	13½
Whiteball–Exeter (pass)	17½	17
Total distance – 173.8 miles	163	169½

Following these trial No 10203 worked the usual roster either to Exeter or Weymouth, putting in one week on the Golden Arrow in March 1955. However between February and July all five

After transfer to the London Midland Region No 10203 worked a variety of services, and is seen here at Watford in November 1960 on an up local train. *British Rail*

locomotives were transferred back to the London Midland Region.

Some Southern Region comments on the engine problems before their final transfer included the following:

1 *Turbochargers.* Poor sealing arrangements led to exhaust blowback at low load, thus fouling the compressors and the bearing lubricant. This was later overcome by air pressure bled from the braking system, but this could not be applied on the first four Mk I engines.
2 *Fuel system.* Fuel pump starvation was caused by the gravity feed not supplying adequate pressure in the fuel rail; this was later overcome by an engine-driven pump to pressurise the fuel rail. Leakage from the high-pressure pipes to the injectors caused dilution of the lubricating oil. The fuel pumps were not pre-calibrated and had to be set individually; this was difficult to achieve in the depots and caused erratic running. The leak from the injectors went to a tank which also carried the spillage of oil and water; this tank had no proper overflow and spilled onto the bogies, causing fires.
3 *Load Regulator.* This was controlled by cam-operated switches behind the governor which were very inaccesible and difficult to adjust.
4 *Exhaust pipes.* On the first four engines there were labyrinth type expansion joints which leaked oil and caused fires. Bellows joints on the Mk II engine cured this problem, but this type could not be fitted to the earlier engines without a redesign of the exhaust manifolds.
5 *Crankshaft seals.* These passed engine oil through to the main generator due to excess crankcase pressure caused by piston blowby. This was improved by leading the crankcase breather into the fan compartment.
6 *Camshaft drive.* This has been mentioned already and was due to the problems caused by chain stretch requiring frequent adjustment. Also a slack chain would put one bank of the VEE out of timing with the other thus causing excess temperatures in half the cylinders.

After the trio transferred to the LM Region they were put on a variety of duties such as to Birmingham, Manchester, and the Anglo-Scottish services, with frequent spells on locals to Bletchley, and occasional runs on the Derby line. Long spells in Derby works in 1956 and 1959 were caused by problems with engine spares since the Mk I engines had been out of production for some time.

Following their visits to Derby works they were based at Willesden and worked main line trains in the summer months, transferring to freight during the winter, because of the poor train heating facility.

In 1962 they were due for a further major overhaul with mileages at 750,000 for No 10201, 600,000 for No 10202 and 480,000 for No 10203, and all were returned to Derby. Since the LMR by that time had an ample supply of new Class 40 locomotives, the three Southern models were kept in storage until 1968 when they were scrapped along with No 10000 by J. Cashmore at Great Bridge.

CHAPTER ELEVEN

THE FELL – NO 10100

The Fell locomotive No 10100 was the only high-powered diesel-mechanical (not diesel-hydraulic) to be produced by British Rail and it was completed at Derby late in 1950. It was a joint project of the London Midland Region of British Railways under H. G. Ivatt, then the chief mechanical and electrical engineer of that Region; Lt Col Rudston Fell of Fell Developments Ltd, and Shell Petroleum, which helped with development finance.

There were three fundamental principles incorporated in this design:

1. The use of mechanical transmission in order to eliminate the losses in the main generator and in the traction motors of a diesel-electric system, thus putting a higher proportion of the engine output to the wheels.
2. The use of a multi-engined arrangement driving through slip couplings and differential gears by which the number of engines in use could vary the transmission ratio.
3. The use of a variable boost to the diesel engines to produce a high torque at low speed with reduced loadings on the engines at top speed.

The engines selected were four Davey Paxman 12RPH units of 7in bore by 7.75in stroke running at up to 1,500rpm with a nominal rating of 500hp. In addition to these four engines there were two AEC 6-cylinder A210D engines, 120mm bore by 140mm stroke running up to 1,800rpm, driving the Holmes-Connerville superchargers, the water circulating pumps, the battery-charging dynamos

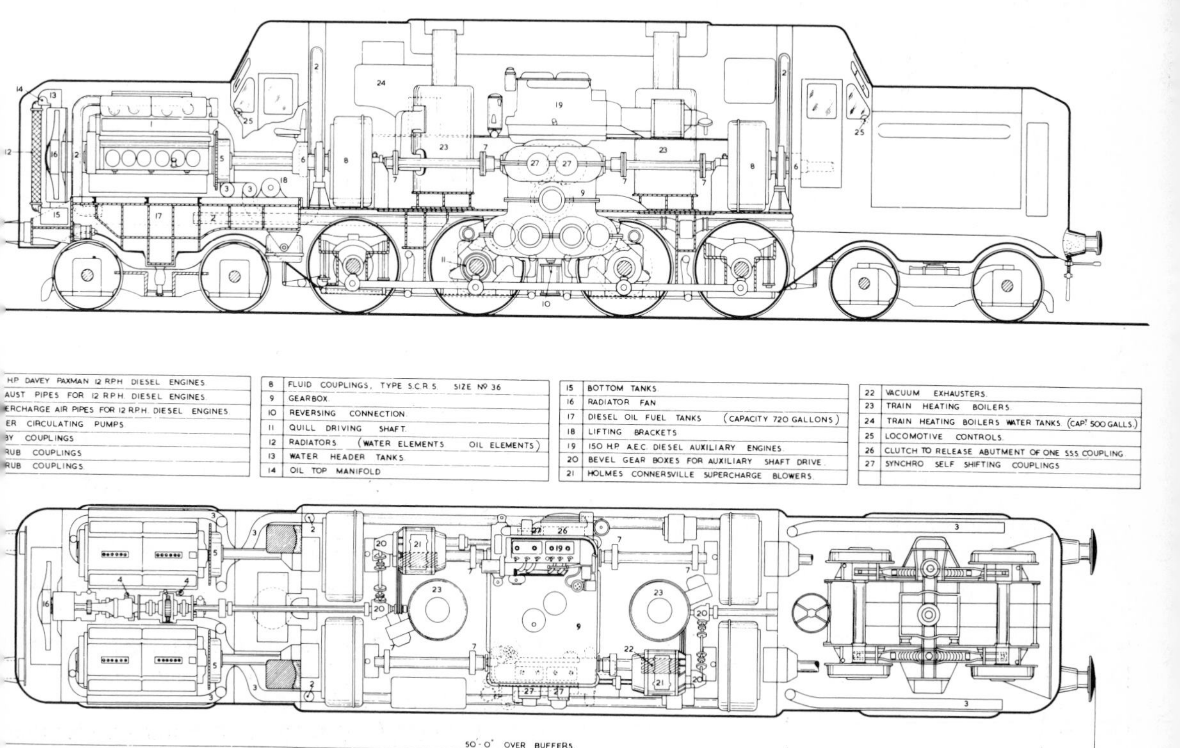

Layout of Prototype Locomotive (British Railways No 10100)

and the radiator fans. These latter engines also operated with variable boost, and worked over a speed range of 1,300rpm to 1,800rpm.

The main engines (E1–4) were arranged two at each end of the locomotive, each fed through a Wellman-Bibby coupling to the input side of a Vulcan-Sinclair hydraulic coupling (H1–4) of the scoop controlled size 36 variable filling type from which the output shafts fed to a differential in the main gearbox (right). The output from the gearbox was taken to the inner pair of four driving wheels of 4ft 3in diameter, in a rigid frame with a bogie at each end thus making a 4–8–4 arrangement. Outside coupling rods drove the outer driving axles. There were two driving cabs with pneumatic controls operated from the vacuum braking system, and there were intended to be two train heating boilers, but because the design was carried out by the steam side at Derby the electrics were kept to a minimum, and there was only sufficient generating capacity to supply one boiler.

The rated brake mean effective pressure (bmep) on the main Paxman engines was 190 lb/sq in at 500 rpm, falling to 75 lb/sq in at 1,400rpm, and that on the AEC auxiliary engines was 150 lb/sq in at 1,300rpm falling to 80 lb/sq in at 1,800rpm, but the maximum firing pressure was kept down to 1,070 lb/sq in and the result was to produce a tractive effort/speed curve as shown left. This also shows similar curves for the 2,000hp diesel-electric locomotive No 10203 and for a BR Class 7 Britannia Pacific; the superiority of the Fell performance is shown between 30mph and 65mph, but the performance falls off completely above and below these speeds.

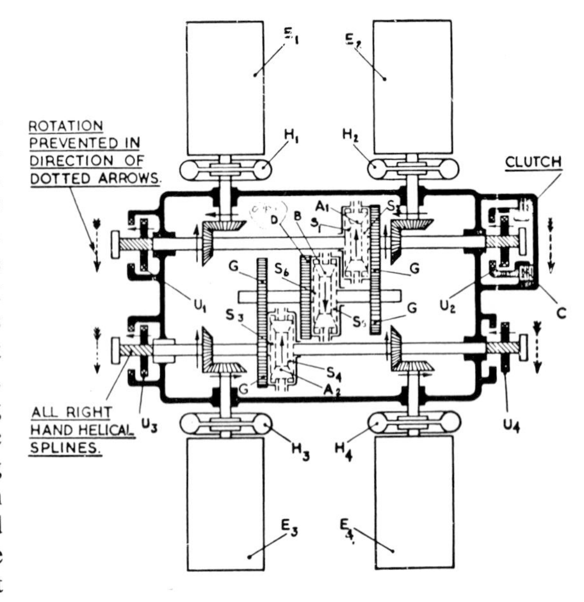

Diagrammatic plan of gearbox

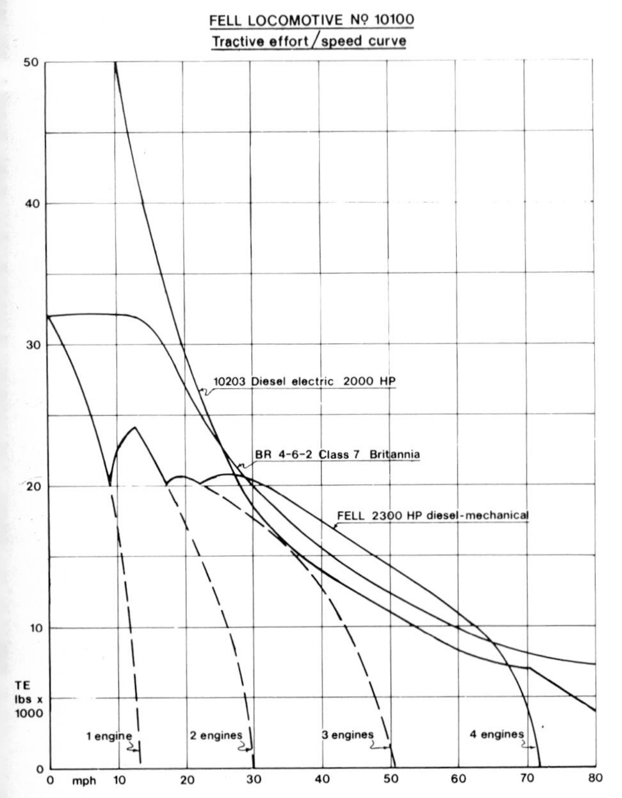

The engine coupling arrangements into the gearbox were designed so that each differential acted as a 2/1 gear ratio and the speed reduction ratios were:

1 engine engaged 0–10mph	4/1 reduction
2 engines engaged 10–17mph	2/1 reduction
3 engines engaged 17–22mph	1.3/1 reduction
4 engines engaged 22–72mph	1/1 reduction

Unless the fluid couplings were filled the output shafts were locked by the synchro self-shifting clutches (U1–4) and the differential cages rotated until the couplings were filled and the corresponding clutches released.

When each fluid coupling was filled under the driver's control, the drive was taken up without any shock, and this applied throughout the speed range. Any engine could be selected to start or to come in at the appropriate operating speed.

The main gearbox was built at Derby with the gears provided by David Brown Ltd. The lower section of the gearbox contained the final drive train of gears and the reversing dog clutches; a warning light indicated which dog clutch was engaged and these could only be moved when at rest. The final drive was through two hollow quills running in white-metal bearings at each end of the lower section of the gearbox housing.

It had been intended for the engines to be arranged so that they could be lifted out easily for maintenance or replacement, but in the final design the nose ends were not long enough to allow for this and a vertical lift was prevented by the location of the cab bulkheads. Since the whole design made for a relatively short overall length, a small increase in the nose length would have allowed for this feature, but for some reason the total length was limited to 50ft.

The locomotive was completed in December

Detail of the gearbox of the Fell diesel-mechanical 4–8–4, BR No 10100. *National Railway Museum*

View of the gearbox mounted on the driving wheels, prior to completion of the locomotive. *British Railways LMR*

The four main engines mounted on the main frames. *British Railways LMR*

1950, and after some proving runs it was found that the storage capacity of the vacuum system was inadequate to deal with both controls and brakes, and it had to be increased. Steam separators also had to be fitted at each engine water outlet in order to prevent the formation of steam pockets which caused poor water circulation.

In January 1951 No 1 end reversing dog clutch seized due to insufficient clearance on the splines and both clutches were returned to the makers for rectification. At the same time the presence of lead/bronze in the gearbox oil indicated problems with the planet wheel bearings; the clearances were increased with better oil feed and improved oil grooves. Similar problems also showed up again in May, by which time only 100 miles had been run.

In September an engineer from Shell called at Derby to inspect the lubricants in the axlebox bearings of No 10100 and was told that this had already been seen to. In fact it had only been done on No 10001, and 10100 went out with nearly dry axleboxes which resulted in a complete seizure on the main line at Kettering, some 56 miles on the way to London. In the original press handout it was stated, 'there is no danger of the train being stalled provided at least one engine is functioning'. After much discussion an attempt was made to move the locomotive in this condition which resulted in the side rod cranks being displaced by several degrees with considerable overloading of the gearbox. (If only the lubricants engineer had called it the Fell instead of 10100 this mistake would have been avoided.)

In July 1952 after some 35,000 miles of operation one of the $\frac{3}{4}$in securing screws of the secondary differential dropped out into the teeth of the reversing wheels when running at 50mph. This resulted in considerable damage to every component in the lower half of the gearbox. Fortunately the casing was undamaged, but all the bearings (about 50) had to be renewed and shafts reclaimed by plating where necessary. This kept the locomotive in the works for about 20 months awaiting material. To prevent a recurrence, the reversing gears were changed to rotate outwards and the final drive gears protected by a shield.

In order to release any locked-up forces in the

No 10100 at Derby. *W. Philip Conolly*

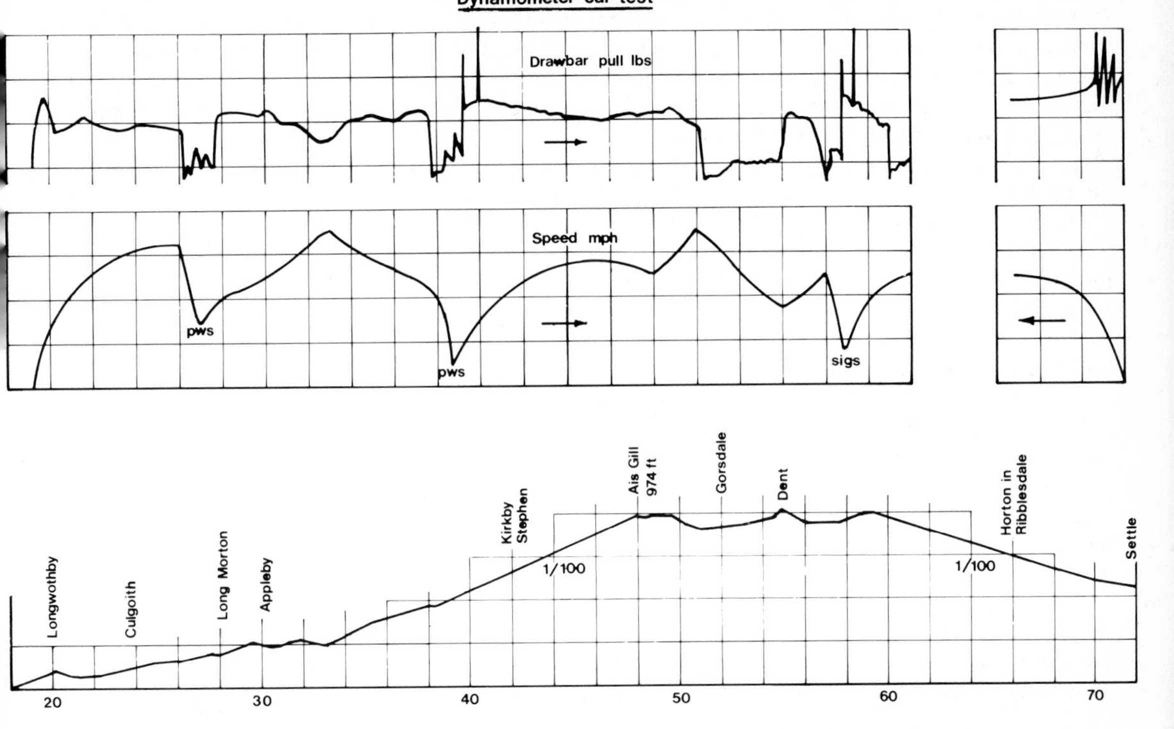

gearbox due to 'buffering', one of the engine clutches was connected through a Swiss Locomotive Manufacturers (SLM) oil-operated clutch under the driver's control. Originally this had 'Ferodo'-lined plates but these had insufficient torque capacity, which resulted in overheating and buckled plates. One of the weekly maintenance tasks was the straightening of these plates. This device was replaced by an oil-operated clutch supplied by Modern Wheel Drive Company, fed with oil from the gearbox lubrication system at 65 lb/sq in, and this problem was cured.

In March 1954 one engine overspeeded to above 1,900rpm when coasting downhill. A broken setscrew in one of the fuel pumps had kept the fuel rack in the open position. The engine suffered no apparent damage, but the valve springs and big-end bolts were replaced for safety. It was found that the fuel racks vibrated at full speed due to the governor drive being remote from the flywheel, thus causing cyclic vibrations. An inertia damper was then attached to the fuel racks and a modified servo piston fitted to the governor. The overspeeding did however strain the fluid coupling casings and heavier ones were fitted to all four couplings.

During the first six months in regular traffic during 1952 the greatest loss in operating time was caused by the bearings in the coupling rods. This was probably due to locked up stresses between the centre rods and the gearbox; removal of these centre rods eliminated this problem.

The train heating apparatus was unsatisfactory as on all the early diesel main line locomotives, and even on many of the later standard production fleet. Originally two units each with an output of 700 lb of steam per hour were planned, but owing to the inadequate electrical supply, only one boiler was installed, and this was uprated to 1,000 lb per hour. It took over 50 minutes to warm up a train of 11 coaches from cold, and on later tests the boiler was only delivering 580 lb per hour. The boiler auxiliaries could drain the battery if not carefully watched, and a further electrical problem was caused by the starting of the auxiliary AEC engines, since those were permanently coupled to their loads which the battery had to turn when starting. Flat batteries were a continual source of trouble.

There were two other principal weaknesses. The first was due to inadequate braking capacity; this was intended to be 47 percent but in practice only worked out at 23 percent which limited operation to passenger and fitted freight trains. The second was caused by poor venting arrangements to the fuel tanks which meant that in spite of carrying 720 gallons the lcomotive would not run the round trip from St Pancras to Manchester and back. This should have needed only 400 gallons, but the locomotive had to be refuelled by hand from the platform at Derby on its way through. Extra vents were later provided to overcome this trouble.

In March 1954 some dynamometer car trials were carried out on the steeply-graded Midland main line from Carlisle to Leeds. The test results taken between Langwathby (20 miles from Carlisle) and Settle (71 miles from Carlisle) showed that in conformity with the te/speed curve (p. 68), the dynamometer car results were as shown on p. 71, which indicate the ability to take a 385-ton load up a 1 in 100 gradient at 50mph. The run was spoiled by slacks for signals and the usual permanent way repairs, but was otherwise very satisfactory.

These tests were carried out using the LMR mobile test plant, which consisted of a dynamometer car fitted with Amsler recording equipment, and up to three mobile test vehicles; these were electric motor coaches with two motor bogies equipped for rheostatic braking. Each axle drove an alternator which was excited by a diesel generator set, and these could be loaded up to simulate additional train weights or gradient as required.

The tests on the Fell were carried out with two of these coaches set to simulate 390 tons, and the results showed that the output of the four engines was 2,230hp. The continuous output at the drawbar developed at 43mph was 1,895hp, and the gearbox temperature did not rise above 154°F. Fluid temperatures in the slip couplings were measured by running at 30.5mph, at which speed the third engine was running at 542rpm with 14 per cent slip, and the fourth engine at 603rpm with 7 percent slip. The maximum fluid temperature was 144°F. No oil coolers were provided for either the couplings or the gearbox and none was deemed necessary.

The engine outputs were measured as follows:

500rpm	420hp
600rpm	470hp
700rpm	510hp
800rpm	540hp
900rpm	565hp
1,000rpm	570hp
1,100rpm	570hp
1,200rpm	555hp
1,300rpm	535hp
1,400rpm	480hp
1,500rpm	300hp

Gearbox overall efficiencies were 95 percent at 36mph and 99 percent at 68mph. Fuel consumption worked out at 0.56 lb/dbhp hr against that of 0.54 lb/dbhp hr for the 2,000hp diesel-electric No 10203.

After completion of the dynamometer car trials the Fell went back into regular service, but as the train heating facility was inadequate for main line duties, its operation was confined to local semi-fast trains between Derby and Manchester (Central). While at the latter station in the summer of 1958 a severe fire in the boiler unit caused extensive damage to the locomotive, and it was withdrawn from service after running about 80,000 miles.

There was a strange similarity between No 10100 and the Paget produced at Derby in 1910. Both had multi-cylinder arrangements (the Fell had 60 cylinders); both had a measure of private finance, and both had gears supplied by David Brown Ltd. Both seized on the main line, effectively blocking it for some time, but the Fell did achieve some revenue-earning operation.

Technically the Fell achieved what it was designed to do, but it was too complicated and spoiled by poor design details such as brakes and heating boiler. Like most non-steam locomotives of that era it spent too much time in the repair shops. Its average annual mileage of just over 13,000 miles reflects these problems. The design was not repeated.

CHAPTER TWELVE

DELTIC

Although the name *Deltic* was applied to a locomotive, it was originally applied to the diesel engines installed within it. Delta, △, the Greek letter 'D' was used because the engine was of triangular shape in cross-section, though in fact the other way up. The design was based on the Junkers Jumo opposed-piston diesel engine used in German aircraft, and a design for a four bank engine to give an output of 2000hp had been conceived but never completed.

D. Napier & Sons Ltd of Acton, a member of the English Electric Group, which had been co-operating with Junkers since 1930, had been asked by the Admiralty in 1946 to produce a lightweight high-output diesel engine for use in patrol boats. By 1952 two of these engines had been built and fitted in a captured German E boat for test and evaluation. These were the D18-11B 18-cylinder 3-bank engines, producing 2500hp at 2000rpm crankshaft speed. The three crankshafts were coupled through a phasing gear that could be used to give a range of output speeds to suit the application required. The original engines in the E boats had been the Daimler-Benz 20-cylinder type giving 2,000hp for 15 minutes only at that output.

With the threat of competition from lightweight high-powered diesel-hydraulic locomotives, the potential of a high-powered lightweight diesel-electric looked possible to English Electric by using two of these Napier Deltic engines. The two Deltic engines would weigh only 20,130lb against the 40,800 lb for their other most powerful engine, the 16SVT, at that time giving only 2,000hp. The Deltic naval rating was only intended for outputs of not more than 60 minutes with overhauls or replacement after 1,000 hours of operation. For rail traction it was essential to establish a rating that would last for at least 6,000 hours between overhauls, corresponding to the time a locomotive would run between tyre turning.

After detailed calculations relating to thermal and mechanical loadings, a continuous traction rating of 1,650hp at 1,500rpm was arrived at; the engine build in this form was known as the D18-25B.

With this rating and by using two engines a locomotive rating of 3,300hp could be obtained, thus making it the world's most powerful diesel-electric locomotive at that time. The whole equipment could be arranged on to a Co-Co wheel arrangement with a total weight of 106 tons and an axle load of not more than 18 tons, thus permitting wide route availability and a maximum speed of 100mph, though it was originally geared for only 90mph.

Each engine drove an English Electric 6-pole main generator type EE831A with a rating of 1,100kW and a maximum output of 3,000A, on top of which was a saddle-mounted auxiliary generator of 45kW driven from the top gear of the phasing train.

The two main generators were series-connected and had duplex lap windings which were supposed

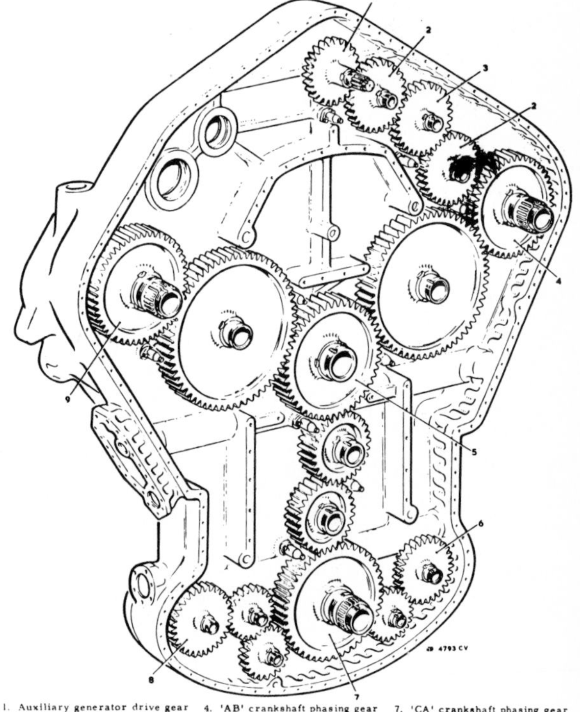

1. Auxiliary generator drive gear
2. Idler gears
3. Governor drive gear
4. 'AB' crankshaft phasing gear
5. Output gear
6. Pressure-oil pump gear
7. 'CA' crankshaft phasing gear
8. Scavenge-oil pump gear
9. 'BC' crankshaft phasing gear

To facilitate cross-references each component bears the same annotation number in Fig 1 7 as in Fig 1-6 The broken numerical sequence in the above key is therefore unavoidable.

Phasing gears (industrial and rail traction engines)

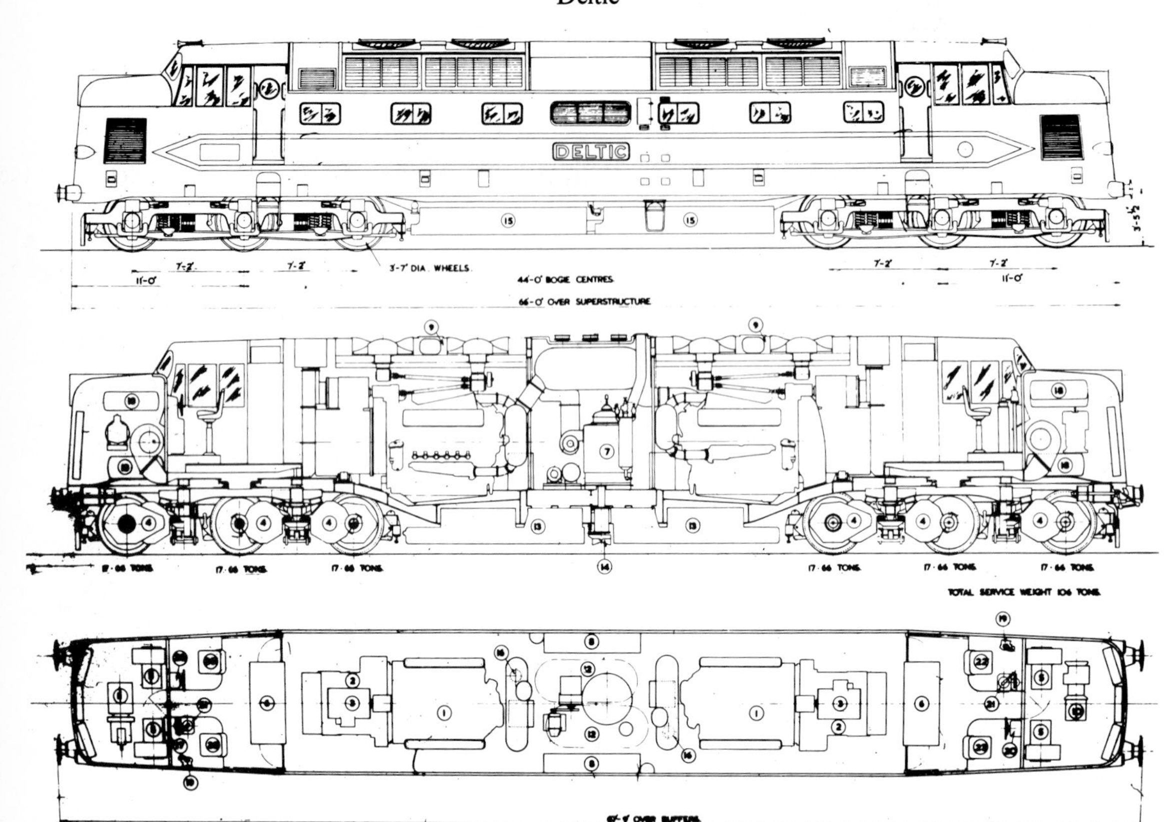

(*Above*) The general layout diagrams of the *Deltic* prototype 3,300hp diesel-electric.

(*Below*) Side view of engine and generator set of the *Deltic*. *Brian Webb Collection*

The *Deltic* under construction, showing details of the bodywork. *GEC Traction*

to produce better commutation at high speeds; this was later found to be in error and single lap winding was adopted for the later versions. They drove the six traction motors which were nose-suspended, axle-hung, force-ventilated, 6-pole, type EE526/A with a continuous rating of 400hp. These were connected in series pairs in three parallel circuits across the main supply. In the event of one power unit being out of action, all six traction motors could still be used at half voltage. The 6-pole construction was found to cause extra maintenance and was later dropped in favour of the standard 4-pole form.

With a power unit almost over each bogie, the main frame could be considerably lighter than with a massive centrally mounted engine, and a stressed bodyside helped to reduce weight further. The standard English Electric design of nose end was adopted in which were mounted the traction motor blowers, a motor-driven compressor in No 1 end, and a two-speed rotary exhauster for the train vacuum brakes in No 2 end. A Vapor-Clarkson train heating unit with a steam output of 2,000 lb/hour was mounted between the two main engines; this was very difficult to reach in an extremely noisy engine room, which did not make for good maintenance conditions.

The radiator and fans were roof-mounted, the fans (two per engine) being driven mechanically by shafts from the same output shaft as for the auxiliary generator. These radiator and fan units could be taken away complete to allow the power unit to be lifted out, as it was intended that engine maintenance should be carried out on an exchange basis. The exhaust from each engine bank fed first into a drum tank and thence to a roof-mounted silencer with its outlets angled so as to miss any overhead electric wires. The control cubicles were placed between the main generators and the drivers' cabs, but the original bulkheads were inadequate, thus making the drivers' cabs excessively noisy.

The bogies were remarkably similar to those used on the LMS No 10000, except that the equaliser bars were mounted below the axle boxes. They had fabricated box-section side members with transoms and headstocks rivetted on. The axleboxes were of the Timken roller-bearing type. Between the bogies were two water tanks for train heating, having a total capacity of 600 gallons, and between these tanks was a water pick-up device for use if required over the water troughs then installed on the main lines. On the outside of the water tanks were the fuel tanks having a capacity of 800 gallons, sufficient for around 600 miles. These

The completed locomotive, in works undercoat.
GEC Traction

tanks were fabricated from light alloy steel and suspended on flexible mountings; the water tanks were also steam-heated as a frost precaution.

The chassis was built up of four main longitudinals, the inner pair being fabricated flanged girders and the outer ones rolled-steel channels. Nineteen cross-sectional members of various shapes joined these longitudinals, including the buffer beams, and the whole was decked on top with adequate drainage facilities to prevent any spillage of oil or water onto the bogies.

The superstructure was welded, using alloy steel, and was insulated and lined internally. Louvred and filtered intakes were provided for the air to the engines, generators and traction motors. A fitting for a large Tonum headlamp was provided in each nose as it was hoped that demonstrations could be arranged on overseas railway systems. There were however few railways where such high-powered locomotives could be used, and most of these were in countries where there was already a diesel engine industry and which would be unlikely to adopt such an elaborate and expensive piece of motive power.

The finish was in light blue with yellow stripes on sides and nose ends, with the motif *DELTIC* on each side below the engine air intakes. There were however some ice cream vans in a similar livery operating around Kings Cross while the *Deltic* was there, resulting in its being known as 'The Ice Cream Wagon'.

The *Deltic* was designed and built at the Preston works of English Electric (formerly Dick, Kerr Ltd) and was completed in October 1955. Following some initial proving trials it was put into service on fast freight duties between Liverpool (Speke) and London (Camden). One passenger turn on the 13 December was on the up Merseyside Express, 10.10 from Liverpool (Lime Street), and back on the down Shamrock evening boat train from Euston. It was confined to operation to and from Liverpool because the Napier Deltic engines were produced and repaired at the factory on the East Lancs road, and it was arranged for the engines to be removed from the locomotive at the Edge Hill depot if necessary.

Operation was at first confined principally to freight duties as the experience with train-heating boilers on other diesel locomotives had not been very satisfactory – it was considered undesirable to spoil the reputation of such a novel unit by the poor performance of that item. It was also prudent to establish the reliability of the engines and ancillary equipment before putting it on to regular passenger service.

On the type of service originally operated it was found that full power was seldom required and that single-engine working was often adequate. This entailed a re-arrangement of the feed to those loads fed from the auxiliary generators, so that they could all be fed from either set according to which one was then in operation.

After some 12,000 miles the solid disc wheels required turning to remove some shelling of the treads that had taken place. The non-ferrous brake blocks were changed for a cast-iron type, but the result was the same. After two more turnings the wheels settled down to give a further 105,000 miles satisfactory operation before needing further attention.

Some vertical oscillations were very noticeable at 12mph and 52mph, but these were overcome by fitting hydraulic shock absorbers between the equaliser beams and the bogie frames.

The original one-piece air ducts which connected the engine air manifolds to the bodyside filters had shown signs of fatigue cracks due to engine vibration in the 200-hour static test at the makers' works; these had been reinforced, but the cracks reappeared in service. Twice, pieces of fractured ducting caused engine failures, and these ducts were then removed. The engine air then had to be drawn from the engine room, but this was much too hot for the engines because the heat from the main generators exhausted into this compartment – also, it resulted in the train-heating boiler being starved of air. It is customary now for the hot air from the generator to pass through the floor to atmosphere and not into the engine room. Eventually a more flexible 2-piece air duct was adopted, which proved satisfactory in service.

In their initial operation on freight trains between London and Liverpool the engines were only partially loaded for most of the time, and with a 2-stroke engine, particularly of the opposed piston type, combustion at part loads is poor, with considerable emission of exhaust smoke and unburnt lubricating oil. The latter results in heavy smoking and even sparks when load is applied, and was a feature of the production Class 5 Deltics throughout their lives.

Originally, the pistons had a large clearance in order to avoid the possibility of seizures due to load variations, but new pistons with reduced clearance and redesigned oil scraper rings were fitted, with some improvement. Later in 1958 a completely new piston design with a crown of copper/aluminium alloy (95/5) and carrying the compression rings, was screwed on to the aluminium alloy skirt and was a further improvement.

After some nine months' proving in freight service performance tests were carried out with a dynamometer car and three of the London Midland Region mobile test units on the Carlisle to Skipton route where the Fell diesel-mechanical No 10100 had been tested in 1954. These tests took place in August 1956, and the haulage capacity was tested with loads varying from 300 tons to 642 tons. With the latter load a speed of 50mph was maintained on a 1 in 100 gradient with a drawbar output of 2,200hp, but if the normal stock resistance figure of 8 lb per ton is taken at 50mph, the drawbar horsepower required would have been 2,602hp and that was hardly possible. The specific fuel consumption figures were encouraging, the best results being at 50mph where the results on a 400-ton train were 0.57 lb/hp against that of 0.62 for No 10203 (the SR 2,000hp diesel-electric unit).

These tests however failed to show up the high speed potential of this locomotive, and this was never appreciated by the London Midland Region when it went into regular passenger service mainly between London and Liverpool following these tests. It also worked the heavy night sleeper trains between London and Carlisle, but never at more than the regulation 90mph.

Meantime its potential had been appreciated by the Eastern Region who realised that it was 'a racehorse and not a giant bullock' (as Gerald Fiennes put it), and it at last managed to get the locomotive transferred to Hornsey depot in January 1959. The Eastern and North Eastern Regions (as they were then separated) realised that they could not speed up their services with the 2,000hp main line diesels then being supplied, and that the extra power of the *Deltic* would enable a high-speed timetable to be introduced. They immediately asked for it to be re-geared for its maximum potential speed of 105mph and proceeded to try it out. They found out too late that though it had a high route availability from the axle load aspect, certain features such as the brake cylinders and cab footsteps limited its use in some platforms at Kings Cross, Darlington and Newcastle.

With a general speed limit of 90mph *Deltic* could not work any regular high-speed service, but it soon showed what it could achieve. On 28 February 1959 with a 250-ton train on the 08.20 ex Kings Cross it proceeded to run *up* Stoke Bank at 100mph. This was the stretch of line *down* which A4 Pacific No 4468 *Mallard* had achieved its 126mph in July 1938, ostensibly carrying out 'brake tests'; similar brake tests were carried out by the *Deltic* in March 1959.

On a down run to Grantham emergency stops were made, first at New Southgate from 62.5mph on an adverse gradient of 1 in 200 which took 36.2 sec, and later at Stoke Tunnel on a similar

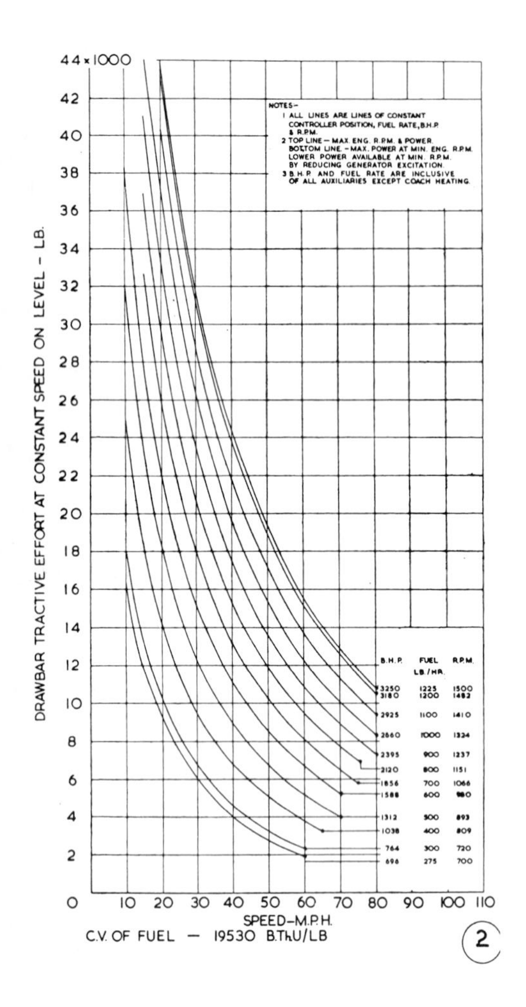

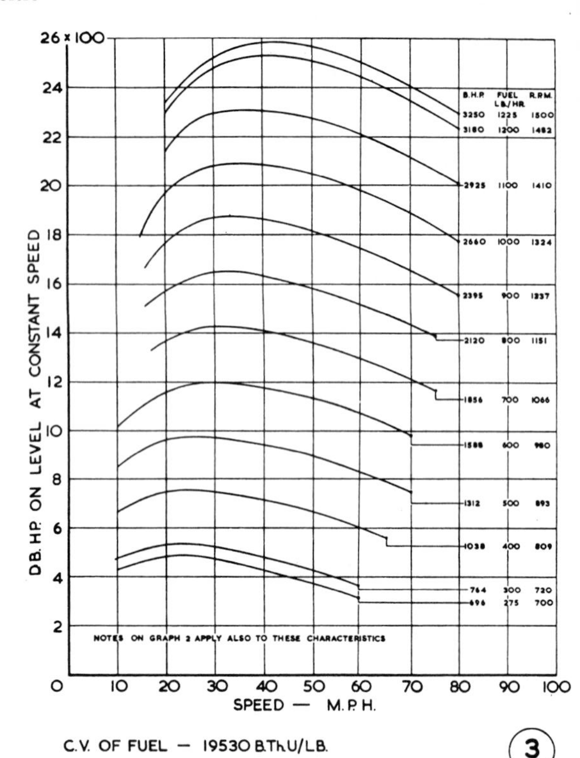

(*Left*) Drawbar tractive effort characteristics. Two engines
(*Above*) Drawbar horsepower characteristics. Two engines

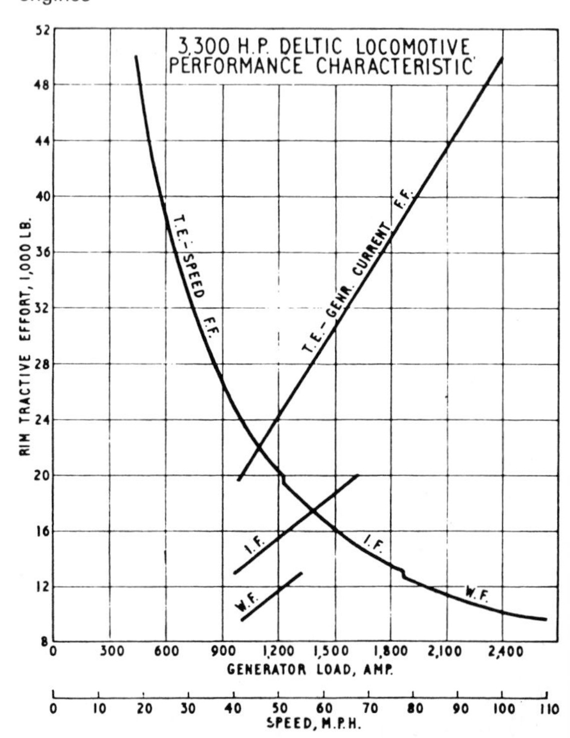

downhill gradient, a stop from 88mph took 65.5 sec in a distance of 5,091ft. The return run in the up direction produced a full throttle acceleration down Stoke Bank from 68mph to 100mph in under five miles. After several miles at 105mph the brakes were applied at 102mph and it took 72.9sec and 6,219ft (1.18 miles) to come to a halt.

These tests were carried out with the vacuum-braked stock of that era, and similar tests in Germany with air-braked stock had shown that a stop could be made in 0.85 mile from 100mph; this may have sparked off the subsequent changeover to air braking for all vehicles in the UK, which had been resisted by the regional general managers at the time the modernisation scheme was introduced in 1955.

On 16 March 1959 the *Deltic* worked to Newcastle, where it dislodged some platform copings at Manors Road station and then lost its footsteps at Darlington. Later with a load of 550 tons it ran from York to Hatfield (170.4 miles) in 149 minutes, and on a test run with 50 freight wagons, weighing 1,146 tons, a run was attempted at 60mph from Doncaster to London, but was thwarted by two hot boxes, one at St Neots and one at Welwyn.

One speed run was arranged in order to demonstrate to permanent way staff the sort of performance the track would have to take. Leaving Huntingdon with a four-coach train, 40mph was reached before the platform was cleared and then the 27 miles to Hitchin were run in 16 minutes, an average of 101.2mph. The East Coast route was no stranger to 100mph running as the A3 and A4 Pacifics frequently topped this in pre-1939 days, but not with an acceleration like this.

The *Deltic* had run some 200,000 miles before coming to the Eastern Region, where it remained for just over two years operating mostly between Doncaster and Kings Cross. It made one or two visits to Scotland and covered around 250,000 miles in these two years. It convinced the East Coast route partners, the Eastern, North Eastern and Scottish Regions that it would meet their requirements and resulted in the production order for the 22 Type 5, later known as Class 55.

It was rumoured that the order had been agreed over lunch between the chairman of the British Transport Commission and English Electric against the wishes of the mechanical engineers who disliked high-speed engines of any sort. They were indeed expensive to maintain, but they enabled the East Coast route to give a service that otherwise could only have been given by electrification, and there was never a chance for that being authorised in those days – not until 1984, in fact.

It was perhaps unfortunate that the prototype was not able to work hard enough to show up some of the faults that developed later, in particular that with the cylinder liners. The operating pressures in an opposed piston engine are particularly severe on the liner since it has no relief in the form of cylinder head bolts, and later stress measurements showed internal pressures up to 25 tons/ sq in. These caused persistent cracking in the weakest point where the injector adaptor fitted. This was improved by a later design of liner, but the problem remained throughout the life of these engines.

It is doubtful if the cost of this prototype, which was reckoned to have been £400,000, was justified, in view of the small order for 22 which resulted, and although English Electric did have the maintenance contract for the engines for most of the life of these locomotives it possibly lost money on that also.

The *Deltic* was withdrawn in March 1961 just as the first of the production models arrived in service, and it is now on display in the Science Museum at South Kensington, London.

Deltic on the LMR at Tamworth Low Level, *W. Philip Conolly*

CHAPTER THIRTEEN

BRUSH *FALCON* NO D0280

The Brush Electrical Engineering Company Ltd had started life in 1855 as Hughes & Marsh, and in 1874 opened the Falcon Iron Works on the site of the present factory. In 1899 the firm was taken-over by Charles Francis Brush, who had come from the USA, to form the Anglo-American Light Corporation – as a result of the electrical infusion, it entered the traction market, building electric tube stock and tramcars for which the firm soon became well known. On coming under the control of Alan Paul Good, and following his purchase of a number of diesel engine builders, it was decided to aim at the main line diesel locomotive market, since this was developing fast for both the electric and diesel engine outlets.

Of the various engines available in the group the only one suitable for main line railway application was the new Mirrlees J range of 9.75in bore by 10.5in stroke running at 900rpm, which had been developed for the Admiralty. This engine had a potential output of up to 2,000hp, but was of welded construction for use in minesweepers.

A working arrangement was also begun with the old-established locomotive building firm of Bagnall of Stafford, which resulted in an order for 25 main line locomotives of 1,000hp for the Ceylon Government Railway in 1951. This model formed the basis of the first order from the British Transport Commission in 1955, at a rating of 1,250hp. The only major change was in the use of a cast-steel bogie in place of the fabricated type that had not proved too reliable in Ceylon.

These first two contracts had shown a reliability and availability figure for the Mirrlees JV engine to be about the same as that for other British diesel engines, but the major problem was that of weight which made this engine uncompetitive for light axleload overseas railways, and limited the power available in the UK to around the 2,000hp range.

As part of the modernisation plan for British Railways, the Western Region had decided to build some diesel-hydraulic locomotives using the Maybach 1,500rpm engine, and Brush had obtained the franchise to build the engine in this country. This arrangement excluded Brush from offering the Maybach engine overseas in diesel-hydraulic locomotives, but not in diesel-electric units. At that time the largest output available from the Maybach engine was 1,600hp, but the light weight enabled a locomotive of 2,800hp to be offered using two of the Maybach 12-cylinder MD655 intercooled engines, which could be built on to a Co-Co wheel arrangement with an axle load of 19.25 tons.

With the two power units and a centrally-mounted train-heating boiler, the overall length worked out at 68ft 10in, but the superstructure weight was kept as low as possible by the use of a Hirondelle type of bridge girder construction; in this Brush had the assistance of the Hawker Siddeley Aircraft experience, since Brush had just become a member of that Group.

Since the use of the high-speed Maybach diesel engine was the key to the layout of this locomotive, some features of the special design and construction of the engine are worth a mention. From its origin as builders of engines for use in the Zeppelin airships, Maybach had produced its first high-speed diesel engines in 1923, and a 12-cylinder engine of 410hp was used in the *Flying Hamburger* in 1932. These first engines used roller bearings for main and big-end bearings, but operating problems led to change when the MD range was designed. In these engines conventional bearings were used for the big-ends with a large roller-borne disc in place of the original small roller mains. These discs were large enough for the crankshaft to be threaded through for removal, and the engine was known as the 'Tunnel' type.

The other novel feature was the adoption of a 6-valve cylinder head with a central combustion chamber and a combined fuel pump and injector unit. The object of this last item was to eliminate the separate injector and the high-pressure fuel pipes which were such a source of trouble in other engines. Other design details included the use of a 2-piece piston, oil-cooled through a telescopic tube, and three lubricating oil circuits, one each for the bearings, for general lubrication, and for the piston cooling; this enabled the oil coolers and filter to be kept down in size to deal with the first two circuits only.

Prior to their use in *Falcon* these Maybach *MD* engines had not been used in any diesel-electric

Brush *Falcon*, No D0280 at Loughborough. *Brush Electrical Engineering Co. Ltd.*

locomotives, and their first application had been in the German V200 diesel-hydraulic locomotives of 2,000hp built by Krauss-Maffei in 1953. The coupling of an electric generator posed some problems of alignment, since there was no way of telling whether the generator shaft was true to the crankshaft. In a conventional engine this can be achieved by taking the crankshaft deflection readings while adjusting the generator housing, but with the Maybach type of crankshaft this could not be done. In order to overcome this problem Maybach produced a type of flexible coupling that it called 'Schwingmetallik'. (The firm used some other rather delightful terms such as 'Schmeirol' for lubricating oil).

With a healthy order book for its Type 2 (Class 31) locomotives, Brush was at last able to spend some money on electrical machine development, and so could design suitable generators and traction motors to suit these engines and their outputs.

In order to control the engine output to suit the generator characteristic a suitable governor had to be adopted, since Maybach's own governor was only suited to the hydraulic output curve, and for this the Woodward PG locomotive governor was selected; there was some opposition from Maybach, but these governors had proved so effective in the other Brush locomotives that the firm insisted on this feature.

The two power units were fitted in 1961. Main generators were of the 6-pole compensated type with class B insulation to BS173, with an output of 910kW at 493V giving up to 1,845A. The auxiliary generators were mounted on top of each main generator and driven by 'Power Grip' drive belts. The six traction motors were 4-pole, force-ventilated units with an output of 373hp at 704rpm, corresponding to 28.5mph. Three stages of field weakening enabled the full power of the engines to be utilised up to 100mph. Each set of three traction motors in one bogie was supplied by the power unit above it.

The weight make-up of the completed locomotive was:-

Diesel engines	13.8 tons
Electrical equipment	32.5 tons
Bogies	27.0 tons
Superstructure and cab	21.5 tons
Radiators and piping. Brakegear	6.4 tons
Boiler and tanks	4.9 tons
Supplies, fuel, water & sand	8.9 tons
	115.0 tons

In the final build considerable attention was paid to the layout in the driver's cab and a new type of 4-digit route indicator was built into the end panels to meet BR requests.

Falcon was completed in December 1961 and first handed-over to the Western Region for dynamometer car trials. These included journeys to Plymouth and tests on the 1 in 37 Lickey Incline between Bromsgrove and Blackwell with train weights of up to 628 tons. On a standing start test on this gradient a tractive effort of 70,300 lb was recorded, while with one power unit only, a train of 457 tons was started on a 1 in 90 gradient with a recorded effort of 26,000 lb.

In April 1962 *Falcon* was transferred to the Eastern Region to follow in the footsteps of A4 Pacific No 60025, which was also *Falcon*. While on the Eastern Region it was stabled at Darnhall Depot, Sheffield, and worked the Sheffield Pullman to and from Kings Cross as well as handling freight traffic to March hauling trains up to 1,800 tons. This latter exercise was not very constructive as the reception sidings could not accomodate trains of this weight and they had to be divided on arrival, blocking the main line.

There was little of note during its time on the Eastern Region except for a fire in one of the cabs caused by a hacksaw blade left in the wrong place, and by the end of 1963 it had achieved a distance of 125,000 miles in various classes of traffic. Being the only unit of that power on the Region at that time it could not be programmed to make proper use of its output, but during its stay none of the trouble later encountered with the cylinder head fractures was experienced; this was claimed to be due to the careful observation of the procedures recommended by the engine makers.

By the end of 1963 it was decided that if *Falcon* was to operate any longer it should be on the Western Region since the other Maybach engines were in use only on that Region. It would also form a useful comparison with the Warship and Western classes then in use on the Region.

Brush offered the locomotive on hire to BR, with all the electrical maintenance to be at the company's expense, at a figure of £8,750 per annum, provided it attained 80,000 miles in the year. It was then overhauled at the Brush works and sent to Swindon for acceptance tests and the fitting of AWS in January 1965.

In February it was stationed at Bristol and commenced to work Type 4 diagrams, but by April No 2 engine had failed twice due to the fracture of water jackets, and *Falcon* went back to Swindon for a top overhaul of both engines and a thorough overhaul of the cooling system. At the same time tyres were turned, springs reset and an overhaul given to the train-heating boiler, the compressors and exhausters. The water scoop was

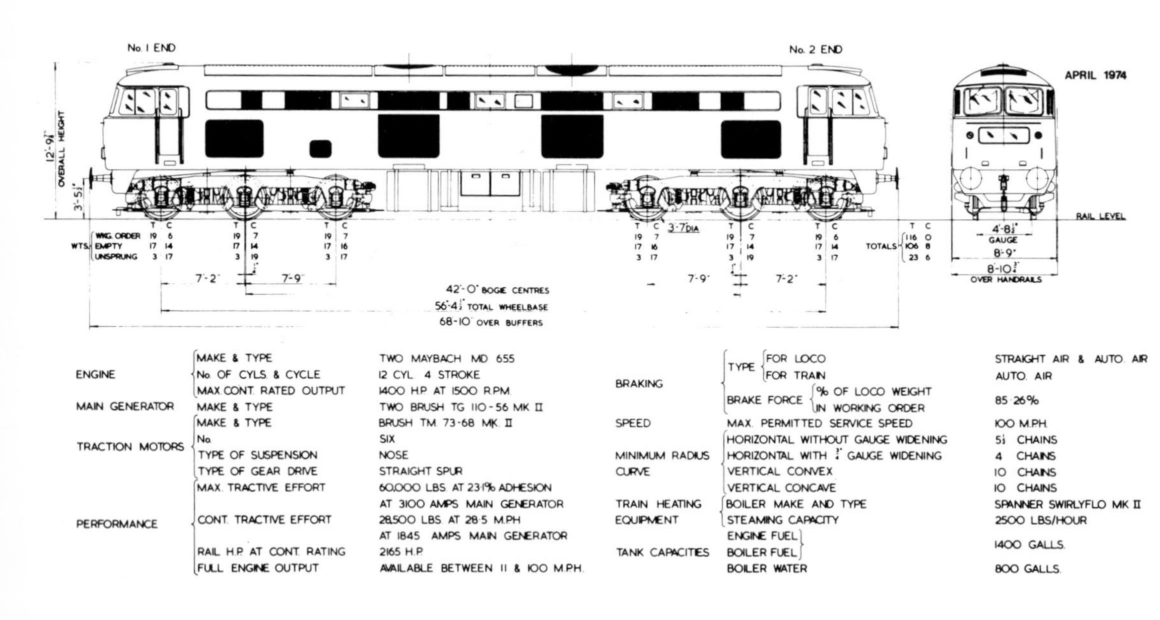

ENGINE	MAKE & TYPE	TWO MAYBACH MD 655
	No. OF CYLS. & CYCLE	12 CYL. 4 STROKE
	MAX. CONT. RATED OUTPUT	1400 H.P. AT 1500 R.P.M.
MAIN GENERATOR	MAKE & TYPE	TWO BRUSH TG 110-56 MK II
TRACTION MOTORS	MAKE & TYPE	BRUSH TM 73-68 MK. II
	No.	SIX
	TYPE OF SUSPENSION	NOSE
	TYPE OF GEAR DRIVE	STRAIGHT SPUR
PERFORMANCE	MAX. TRACTIVE EFFORT	60,000 LBS. AT 23·1% ADHESION AT 3100 AMPS MAIN GENERATOR
	CONT. TRACTIVE EFFORT	28,500 LBS. AT 28·5 M.P.H AT 1845 AMPS MAIN GENERATOR
	RAIL H.P. AT CONT. RATING	2165 H.P.
	FULL ENGINE OUTPUT	AVAILABLE BETWEEN 11 & 100 M.P.H.
BRAKING	TYPE FOR LOCO	STRAIGHT AIR & AUTO. AIR
	TYPE FOR TRAIN	AUTO. AIR
	BRAKE FORCE % OF LOCO WEIGHT IN WORKING ORDER	85·26%
SPEED	MAX. PERMITTED SERVICE SPEED	100 M.P.H.
MINIMUM RADIUS CURVE	HORIZONTAL WITHOUT GAUGE WIDENING	5½ CHAINS
	HORIZONTAL WITH ¾" GAUGE WIDENING	4 CHAINS
	VERTICAL CONVEX	10 CHAINS
	VERTICAL CONCAVE	10 CHAINS
TRAIN HEATING EQUIPMENT	BOILER MAKE AND TYPE	SPANNER SWIRLYFLO MK II
	STEAMING CAPACITY	2500 LBS/HOUR
TANK CAPACITIES	ENGINE FUEL, BOILER FUEL	1400 GALLS.
	BOILER WATER	800 GALLS.

General diagram of *Falcon* in its later guise as BR Class 53 No 1200.

also removed. It returned to service in August, but in September the No 2 engine had two further failures due to fractured cylinders blocks, and in December there were three cracked cylinder heads. That year it only covered 29,400 miles.

In 1966 it had three sojourns in Swindon, the first due to water in No 3 cylinder fracturing a connecting rod, this time in No 1 engine. The loss was 92 days, but the mileage was better at 57,500 or 210 miles per working day. During 1967 it rested in Swindon for 144 days, 61 of which were due to burnt-out controls in the boiler panel. Mileage that year was 46,000. Diagrams worked included the 09.15 Bristol to Paddington, 13.45 Paddington to Bristol, 17.15 Bristol to Paddington and the 22.00 Paddington to Bristol on the Penzance postal. Daily mileage again averaged 210 miles. 1968 was the best year and the mileage covered was 90,400 against an average of 85,000 for the Class 42 Warships. Miles per casualty worked out at 7,500 and the only serious defect was a failed turbocharger bearing just before Christmas.

In August 1968 it had been proposed to withdraw *Falcon* from service due to the introduction of Mk II air-braked coaches (Any excuse to get rid of a prototype), but BR decided to remove the exhausters and to equip the locomotive for dual air braking. At the same time negotiations were proceeding to terminate the hiring agreement and to purchase it outright for £20,000. The estimated cost of the conversion together with a further overhaul of the mechanical parts was £43,000. This was authorised in April 1970 and *Falcon* enjoyed a further visit to the operating table and convalescence until December when it emerged in BR colours, numbered 1200, and given a class of its own, Class 53.

During December 1970 and January 1971 a series of trials was undertaken between Swindon, Old Oak and Didcot, as well as some high-speed trials between Bristol and Taunton. These were carried out with an 8-coach train, and the time allowed for the 45 miles was 36 minutes. In February another fire in the boiler controls caused a delay until May when the trials were resumed. It was then sent back to Bristol and resumed passenger duties till July 1972 when it was sent to Llanwern for use on freight traffic to Ebbw Vale. This time the boiler was isolated.

No 1200 continued on this service until 1974, achieving about 40,000 miles a year. It was then sent away for some reason to the Brush works at Loughborough. A telephone call from a perplexed station manager at Loughborough pointed out that the rail connection to the Brush works had been removed some two years earlier (!) so *Falcon* was returned to Llanwern.

In October 1975 a traction motor bearing failed, so as had happened to the Brown Boveri gas turbine, this was the reason at last for its withdrawal from traffic. The total mileage achieved since 1961 was just over 550,000, an annual average of nearly 40,000 miles.

Falcon was finally sold to Cashmore for scrap in March 1975 for £5,125. It was a sad end to a brave venture, but another instance where a prototype locomotive proved nothing largely because operating departments rather understandably do not like such locomotives. They mean special crew training, special spares, and usually they only work successfully if a maker's service engineer is on hand most of the time. This was a good locomotive mechanically and electrically, like all Brush locomotives, but the engines were the weak feature. The biggest weakness was in the 6-valve head which was prone to fracture, and this caused loss of water which resulted in overheating, or to water in the cylinders, which caused the flywheel to turn on the crankshaft.

Although Swindon Works was specially equipped to maintain these engines, the two on this locomotive were special since any engine change entailed a change of generating mounting plate as well as the governor. Further, there were no proper testing facilities for a power unit of this output, and tests had to be carried out after fitting in the locomotive.

The lessons from this locomotive were incorporated in the Brush-Sulzer 2,750hp Class 47, of which 512 were later built. The overall cost to BR from 1965 to 1975 would seem to work out at approximately 25p per mile, excluding fuel and daily running costs. The cost to Brush was in the region of £140,000. In the end the only people likely to profit from this venture were the scrap merchants.

CHAPTER FOURTEEN

D0260 *LION*

This was the last of the three large prototype diesel-electric locomotives in the 2,700/2,800hp category to be submitted for trials on British Railways in 1962. The concept had gone back a long way earlier before Sulzer Brothers had received any BR orders, and the company wanted to put its largest engine, the 12LDA28, then rated at 2,300hp, on to a Co-Co wheel arrangement.

When the modernisation programme was initiated in 1955, BR had decided to build in its own works the locomotives in which this engine was going to be incorporated; because of weight the design could not be fitted on to a CoCo wheel arrangment. It was decided therefore to employ the Bolland bogies as used on the Southern Region in order to keep within the permissible axle loads. At that time Sulzer could not find a suitable locomotive builder which could offer this engine on a Co-Co frame, but when Sulzer learned that Brush was proposing to build the 2,800hp *Falcon* using two Maybach high-speed engines, the firm decided to offer a competitive unit with its medium-speed engine.

By then the Sulzer 12LDA28 engine had appeared to be capable of being uprated to 2,750hp, and since a number of the smaller 6-cylinder and 8-cylinder LDA engines had been built into locomotives supplied by the Birmingham Railway Carriage & Wagon Co Ltd of Smethwick, Birmingham, Sulzer decided to co-operate with that company in the building of a suitable prototype.

The electrical equipment used in the other Sulzer/BRCW locomotives had originally been supplied by the British Thompson Houston Co Ltd of Rugby, which had amalgamated with Metropolitan-Vickers of Manchester in 1959, to become part of the Associated Electrical

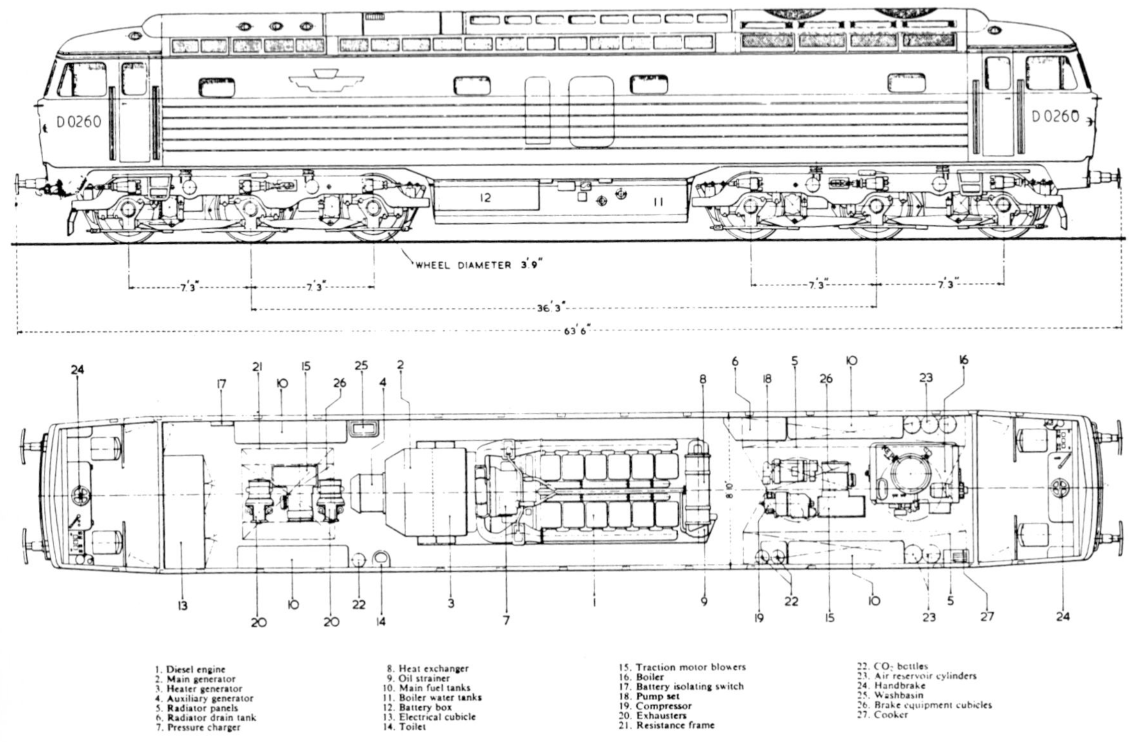

Layout of equipment, and general dimensions of BRCW/Sulzer/AEI 2750hp Co-Co diesel electric locomotive D0260 *Lion*

(*Above*) General ¾-view and overhead view of the bogie as used on D0260 *Lion. AEI Ltd.*

(*Below*) Cross-section of the 12LDA28 engine built by Sulzer Brothers. *Sulzer Brothers*

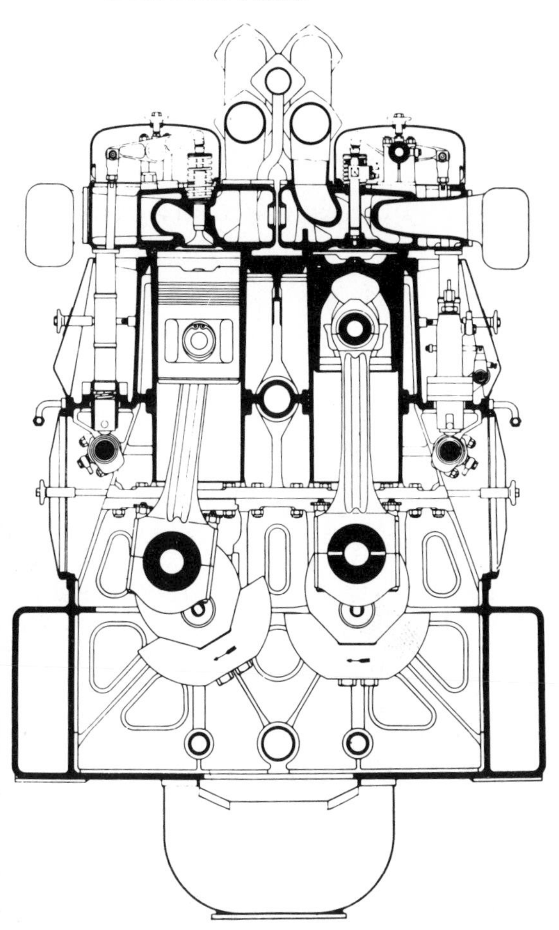

Industries Ltd. AEI agreed to supply the electrical portion of the locomotive and the design basis was complete.

The overall design (p. 84) was an ambitious project in attempting to accomodate a diesel engine weighing 22.3 tons into an overall weight of 114 tons in order to keep to the 19-ton stipulated axle load. In addition electric and steam systems for train heating were both included in the specification. The engine weight compares with the 13.8 tons for the twin Maybach engines in the Brush *Falcon*, and 19.4 tons for the English Electric 16CSVT in DP2. Weight was saved by the use of silicone insulation in the electrical machines and by the use of a light metre gauge traction motors of International General Electric (IGE) design. Lightweight fabricated bogies of Alsthom design were also incorporated. Alsthom was the French side of the Thompson Houston organisation of which BTH was the UK member.

The Sulzer LDA28C engine was naturally heavy since it was of the twin bank construction, each bank having six cylinders with the two crankshafts geared together to drive the generator. In order to achieve the output required, the crankshaft speeds had been raised to 800rpm from the 750rpm previously used on BR and the brake mean effective pressure (bmep) of the engine had been raised to 168 lb/sq in. The crankshaft gearing drove the main and auxiliary generators at 1,150rpm, thus enabling these machines to be smaller and lighter than if they had been at crankshaft speed as was the case with in-line or VEE engines.

The Sulzer LDA28 engine range consisted of 6-, 8- and 12-cylinder models having a bore of 280mm and a stroke of 360mm. It was fitted with a 2-valve cylinder head, and the crankcase consisted of cast steel transverse members welded into a mild steel frame. The 12-cylinder version had been supplied to the French Railways (SNCF) at 2,000hp in 1955; then it was offered to BR in 1955 at 2,300hp and a year later at 2,500hp for use in what were to be the Class 45/46 units. The final uprating was put forward in 1959 to 2,750hp, and a 100-hour type test to the UIC code 623/OR was carried out in June/July 1962. The engine was designed at Winterthur in Switzerland and built by Vickers Ltd at Barrow-in-Furness along with most of the other 1,454 Sulzer engines used on British Railways.

The turbocharger which was of Sulzer's own manufacture was the same as those used on the

12LDA28B engines rated at 2,500hp, but as some turbine blade fractures had occurred on those in service, a lacing wire was used as a damper to eliminate blade resonance. In addition intercoolers were fitted in each inlet manifold, cooled by the engine jacket cooling circuit.

The radiators were roof-mounted, with two electrically-driven fans, the whole built as a single removable unit. The radiators were self-draining to reception tanks within the body as a frost precaution for overnight stabling. The roof portion over the engine compartment was fitted with translucent fibreglass panels and could be lifted 6in to allow heat to escape while work was being done on the engine. This was interlocked so that it could only be raised when the locomotive was stationary and the locomotive could not be moved while it was open. This made for an exceptionally light and airy engine compartment.

The underframe was a welded structure with the bodysides forming the load-carrying members. These were in the form of a Virendeel truss with fluting below the waist level to avoid the uneven appearance often present with welded plates. The driving cabs at each end were fitted with electrically-heated gold film glass front windows, with wipers and washers. The instruments included brake gauges, speedometer and six ammeters, one for each motor circuit, all illuminated by ultra-violet lights. The bulkheads between the cabs and the engine room were 3in thick and insulated with fibreglass wool. The interior was neatly finished in grey and blue with polished timber fascias.

The bogies were the first on BR to incorporate the Alsthom system of twin rubber cone body supports and radius arm guided axleboxes. The bogie frame was fabricated from mild steel and supported on four nests of coil springs on equalising beams carried from the axleboxes on Metalastik rubber pads. The body was carried partly by the two bogie transoms and partly by four adjustable spring-loaded side bearers. The bogie brakes consisted of two clasp type hangers per wheel, each with two renewable cast-iron shoes operated by 8in diameter JSL cylinders and slack adjusters. Ferrobestos bushes eliminated any necessity for lubrication.

In addition to a train-heating winding on the main generator equivalent to 250hp, a Spanner Mk IIIB boiler was fitted capable of an output of 2,500 lb (1135kg) of steam per hour at 50 lb/sq in, supplied from a water tank having a capacity of 1,260 gallons (5,700 litres) and fitted with a briquette cage for water treatment chemicals.

The electrical equipment consisted of a main generator type TG5303 with an output of up to 3,500A combined with a train heating generator type AG106 giving 480A at 800V, and an auxiliary generator type AG105 giving 382A at 110V all with silicone insulation to class H. The six metre-gauge traction motors of AEI Type 253 were force-ventilated and with class H insulation. There were two stages of field weakening, and with a top speed of 1,305rpm, combined with a gear ratio of 17/70, a maximum operating speed of 100mph was available.

BRCW was fairly new to the locomotive business, but produced a remarkably good range of locomotives for BR in Classes 25, 27 and 33. The firm paid a lot of attention to details of bodywork design, such as the location of air filters. BRCW located all the air filters at cantrail level and tests showed that these absorbed an average of 2oz of dust in 25,000 miles compared to 12oz for the filters in the Derby-built Class 24 which had some of their filters low down in the bodyside panels. The engine wear rates were noticeably lower in the case of the BRCW units.

No D0260 had originally been discussed at a meeting held at BTC headquarters on 4 November 1960. It was completed and demonstrated at Marylebone Station in May 1962 with a view to operation on the Eastern Region, but first it went to work on the Western Region in order to undertake some dynamometer car trials.

Following driver training it started regular operation on 14 May, making two round trips a day between Paddington and Wolverhampton, 492 miles a day, but after three days it failed near Leamington due to a severe flashover on the main generator. This was due to an over-wired fuse on the heating generator voltmeter, and the blame was laid on the Sulzer engineers who had been fitting some special test equipment. The generator was repaired and *Lion* was in service again on 25 May.

From then it ran only between Paddington and Swindon, making 160 miles a day, until the dynamometer trials which took place from 24 July to 15 August. The first week was occupied in hauling trains of various weights between 250 tons and 550 tons between Swindon and Bristol. On 8 August a 569-ton train was hauled from Swindon to Plymouth and back, with standing starts on the steepest hill sections between Newton

In 1963 D0260 *Lion* was employed on the Eastern Region, and is seen here on express passenger duty. *GEC Traction Ltd.*

Abbot and Plymouth. The next day trials were carried out with 629 tons on the 1 in 37 Lickey Incline between Bromsgrove and Blackwell on the main line from Birmingham to Bristol. On that occasion the commutation on the main generator was described as poor with heavy sparking, almost to flashover level, and the fault was traced to the voltage regulator for the heating generator which caused a hunting condition in the engine.

Lion was then returned to BRCW for the rectification of these faults, and was not back in service until March 1963, when it took a 20-coach train to High Wycombe, again with heavy sparking on the main generator. Further trials took place in August with 400-ton trains from Birmingham to High Wycombe, and on the Lickey Incline. This time the generator commutation was reported as being good even up to 6,000A which were recorded when starting from rest on the 1 in 37 gradient.

On 9 September *Lion* was transferred to the Eastern Region, travelling via Leeds to Kings Cross, and was stabled at Finsbury Park. It worked main line trains from Kings Cross, including the Yorkshire Pullman to Harrogate, but on 12 November it failed at Newark due to an explosion in the control cubicle when working a freight train from Sheffield. One particular copper strip was heavily overloaded and eventually melted. The control cubicle was rebuilt and the locomotive returned to duty working the Sheffield Pullman, a fairly lightly loaded train. It was working this train on 20 January 1964 when it sustained a severe flashover on the main generator near Huntingdon while travelling at 70mph, though it did manage to finish its journey 15 minutes late.

By this time the engine was suffering from a cracked sump leaking up to 20 gallons of oil per day – this was a problem that was to occur on many of the later Sulzer 12LDA28C engines. There were also several leaks in the water system and the locomotive was returned to BRCW for attention to these defects.

However, just at this time the railway building

side of BRCW was closed down by the bank, which thought that better use could be made of the valuable land on which the works stood, so the firm could undertake no further work on this prototype.

In a summary report issued in January 1964 it was stated that:

> 'the locomotive had always carried out the duties assigned to it. There were only two causes of serious delay, one due to boiler trouble and the other due to a cracked engine sump. There was only one instance of complete failure due to the disintegration of a negative bus bar'.

Certain items in the superstructure had deteriorated, such as screen wipers and door handles. In addition the roof-raising panels had to be re-piped in copper in place of the original plastic piping. The bogies had given a hard ride, and fractures had appeared in the brackets carrying the brake levers.

The engine had been satisfactory apart from the hunting problem and the oil sump, which had cracked twice. There were also problems with leaks in the cooling water system, one of which had flooded the traction motor connection boxes. The traction motors had behaved well, but fractures occurred in the gear cases and the axle oil seals leaked.

The main source of trouble, as usual, was said to have been the train-heating boiler, all due to electrical faults in the control equipment used in this component. BRCW had made an honest attempt to overcome this by providing the electric train-heating facility, but BR at that time did not have sufficient electrically-equipped stock to make use of this facility.

When *Lion* was first shown at Marylebone it was painted white and was known as 'the *White Lion*', but it soon became to be called 'the *White Elephant*'. After running some 80,000 miles it was broken-up at the Attercliffe works of the AEI, which retained the electrical equipment. The engines and radiators were returned to Sulzer Brothers. T. W. Ward quoted £355 for removing and scrapping the body and bogies.

The 'White Lion' No D0260 built by BRCW on trials on the Lickey Incline in 1962 with 638 ton train. The electrical connections to the dynamometer car are visible from the rear engine room window. *GEC Traction Ltd.*

CHAPTER FIFTEEN

DP 2

Of all the prototype locomotives built since 1947 the English Electric DP2 was the most successful operationally, having achieved an average annual mileage during its life of just over 125,000 miles. This was primarily due to the fact that its sole object was to prove the 16-cylinder version of the English Electric 10in bore diesel engine at its new rating of 2,700hp at a brake mean horsepower of 167 lb/sq in. When British Railways placed its first orders under the modernisation scheme in 1955, English Electric offered its 16SVT engine at 2,000hp, the same rating as that installed in No 10203 produced the year before by the Southern Region. At the same time Sulzer was offering its 12LDA28 engine at 2,300hp.

When orders were placed for the second batch of locomotives, English Electric offered a repeat at the same rating, although by improvement in the turbocharger design, a rating of 2,200hp could have been offered; this rating was not offered because it would have meant a new generator design. At the same time Sulzer offered their engine at a rating of 2,500hp, a 10 percent uprating.

By this time it was becoming obvious that higher outputs would shortly be needed in order to produce higher train speeds and to cope with electric train-heating. Experience with the early train-heating boilers compared with the trouble-free electric heating system on the Hastings line diesel-electric multiple units, was an early pointer in this direction, but was largely ignored by BR.

At the same time English Electric was occupied with many projects, including two 500hp shunting locomotives, the prototype *Deltic*, and the Gas Turbine GT3, while its diesel engine division was developing a 1,500rpm engine primarily for the

General layout diagrams of English Electric 2,700hp diesel-electric Co-Co prototype locomotive No DP2.

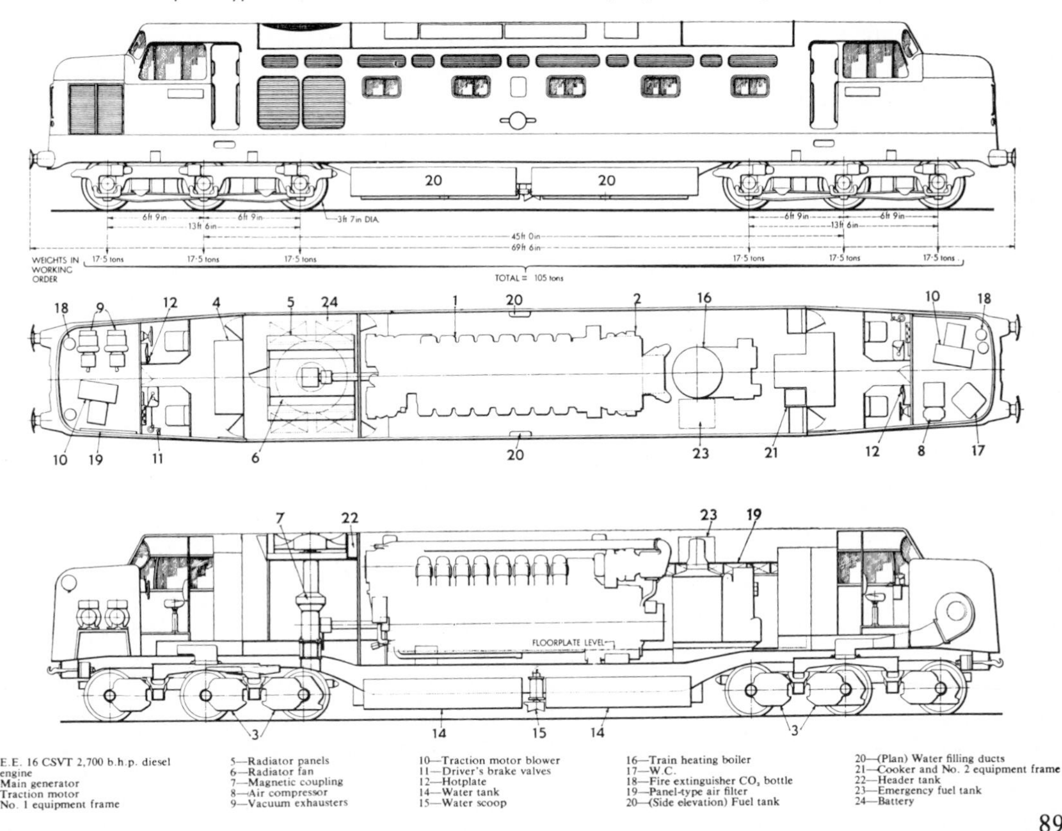

overseas market, as well as a 1,200rpm version of its 10in bore RK range, intended to produce 200hp per cylinder. However, at this stage none of these was ready for offer to BR.

When BR finally requested locomotives of 2,700hp, Sulzer merely stepped-up its 12LDA28 by another 10 percent, but English Electric had to uprate its output from 2,000hp to 2,700hp, and it was felt by BR that this increase was too large to be acceptable without further proving trials.

By then some 12-cylinder versions of the SVT engine range were in operation in a charge-cooled form at the equivalent of the required rating, in Sudan and in East Africa, and a type test of one of these engines had been witnessed by a BR representative, but they were still not convinced. One solution would have been to have carried out a further 100-hour type test to BS2953 (now BS5514) with a 16-cylinder engine. As this would have cost at least £15,000 for wages and fuel, in addition to the engine cost, it was decided that it would be more convincing to instal an engine in a locomotive and to operate it to the satisfaction of BR.

There was in production at that time the batch of 22 Deltic locomotives at 3300hp on a Co-Co wheel arrangement, and it was found that the design of one of these could be modified to accommodate the 16CSVT engine by the use of special lightweight radiators within an axle load of 17.5 tons. The lightweight radiators were necessary since the higher rating could only be obtained by the use of aftercoolers, in order to keep the exhaust temperatures within acceptable limits to avoid the use of special steels in the exhaust manifolds and the turbocharger. To achieve this involved reducing the air temperature from 190°F after the compressor, to 130°F in the inlet manifold, and this meant the use of a separate panel in the radiator set on the outside to receive the cooler air first.

There was not sufficient headroom with the 16CSVT engine to instal roof-mounted radiators as in the Deltic locomotives, and vertical radiator panels were installed at the free end of the engine, with a single fan as on most other English Electric locomotives. This fan speed control was by means of an electro-magnetic slip coupling in the fan drive controlled by the engine jacket water temperature, which also controlled the louvre shutters on the radiator panels. This system of control from the engine jacket circuit only led to one on line failure mentioned later.

In comparing the English Electric 10in bore engine with its Sulzer rival, it suffered from the necessity of having to use 16 cylinders against the 12 of the 280mm bore used by Sulzer, which also meant that Sulzer could use only one turbocharger. English Electric was politically tied to the Napier turbocharger, and the company had no design suitable which would enable less than four turbochargers to be used within the space available. This was later to raise a problem in operation due to the poor distribution of the air for combustion within the engine room.

Basically the engine was the same as the other 16SVT engines then in service on the Type 4 (Class 40) locomotives, but there were some significant differences internally. Apart from the larger turbochargers and the aftercoolers, the crankcase had been strengthened to take the higher firing loads, an improved design of piston was adopted, and though it was not considered necessary to use an oil-cooled piston for this rating, provision had been made for this in the event of further upratings.

Other changes included the use of larger oil filters, larger fuel pumps and injectors, and in the use of a Woodward PG traction governor fitted with a pressure-sensing device to cut back the fuel in the event of any loss of inlet manifold pressure due to a turbocharger failure or a manifold bellows fracture.

Insofar as the rest of the locomotive was concerned, this was conventional English Electric so that any driver trained for its Class 37 or Class 40 types or even a Deltic, could take over this locomotive with virtually no extra training. This made it very acceptable to the operating side, and for good measure it had an adequate train-heating boiler able to warm any train it might be called on to haul.

As mentioned earlier, it was not considered worth carrying out an official 100 hour type test because of the cost and the anomalies of the testing procedure. There were two test standards to which this could have been carried out. One was the British test to BS2953 which called for an inlet water temperature to the aftercooler of 105°F and one set of cyclic variations. The other was a continental one to the UIC procedure OR623 which called for an inlet water temperature of 45°C (113°F), and a different set of cyclic variations. The UIC test also called for much more expensive instrumentation, calibration and supervision, so that unless extensive business

The English Electric 16CSVT power unit. *English Electric Co. Ltd.*

could be expected it was not considered worthwhile undergoing this test. Attempts to marry the two systems met with the usual 'non' from the other side of the Channel. Anyway, prior to handing over to BR the whole locomotive was given the usual English Electric 200-hour cycle test in full working conditions not only to test the engine, but all the auxiliaries and the electrical equipment.

DP2 first ran from the Vulcan Foundry works at Newton-le-Willows to Chester and back on the 2 May 1962, and after some further checks carried out a test run from Crewe to Carlisle and back on the 8 May with a test train of 475 tons. The minimum speed up the 1 in 75 over Shap was 43mph.

Without any further ado DP2 went straight into revenue-earning service operating between Euston and Liverpool. This was one of the London Midland Region traditional testing routes, which had been used for the Turbomotive and the original *Deltic*. The trains worked were the 07.45 from Euston to Liverpool which was usually a 500-ton train, the 14.05 Liverpool to Euston, usually 450 tons followed by the 19.15 Euston to Crewe, and finally the 03.00 Crewe to Euston, giving a weekly mileage of 3,800 miles.

All was going well when tragedy struck out of the blue. A new maintenance shed had been erected at Camden and DP2 was the first to enter this on 19 May; the running rails were raised on supports about 3ft above floor level and on the locomotive's entry some of the supporting pedestals moved outwards, causing DP2 to fall some 14in. A further fall was arrested by the brake gear resting on the rails and it remained there over the week-end until it was rerailed on the Monday and returned to the Vulcan works. It was at first thought that damage might have occurred to the main frame or to the engine, but alignment tests showed these to be alright; the only part that needed replacement was the frame of the damaged No 1 bogie, and by 28 May DP2 was back in service on the Liverpool diagram.

Some observations were then carried out to study the load factor, and it was ascertained that in the three-hour run from London to Crewe, only 27 minutes were on full load and 55 minutes on $\frac{3}{4}$-load. On the up journey from Liverpool to Rugby taking just over two hours, 16 minutes were on full load and 39 minutes on $\frac{3}{4}$-load. These were unusual conditions because so many speed restrictions were then in force due to the electrification works; normally it was usual for most time under power to be spent at full load rather than at partial load.

In June a further trip to the Vulcan works was necessary in order to find the cause of a slow response in the load regulator. This was found to be due to an 'O' ring which had become dry and jammed in its groove. In September, after suffering two further derailments in the Liverpool area, fortunately without damage, DP2 was transferred to the Euston-Carlisle route and worked the 13.25 from Euston, and the 01.31 from Carlisle, giving a weekly distance of 3,600 miles.

One cold night in January 1963 DP2 suffered its first line failure due to the cooling system. Running south near Denbigh Hall in the early morning it was held up by signals for 30 minutes, and though the engine jacket water was warm enough to keep the fan running, there was not enough heat going into the aftercooler circuit under idling conditions, and the water froze in the radiator panel. The damage and resultant loss of water caused the engine to shut down and the locomotive had to be taken out of service.

On another occasion DP2 ran over some platelayers' tools near Tamworth and was stopped for examination. This caused a delay of 12 minutes which was turned into an early arrival at Euston of 14 minutes, thus making up 26 minutes on its journey of 110 miles.

Some trial runs were undertaken between Euston and Glasgow which gave the following results:

Train	*Load (tons)*	*Time (mins.)*	*Load factor (%)*	*Fuel consumption gal/mile*
Caledonian	300	415	55.3	1.22
Midday Scot	400	430	65.3	1.45
Night Sleeper	550	510	64.0	1.70

DP2 at Kings Cross on the Master Cutler.
GEC Traction Ltd.

DP2's successful career was cut short on 31 July 1967, when it was involved in a collision with a derailed cement wagon at Thirsk. Damage was extensive, as the photograph shows.

The average power requirements for the Midday Scot was 1,775hp and for the Caledonian 1,500hp.

In June 1963 DP2 was withdrawn for tyre-turning having completed 164,600 miles in 13 months, and as the engine hours were then 4,500 it was given its 5,000-hour examination. This was more thorough than the usual inspection at that period, but no parts were found to be in need of renewal. The Clayton train-heating boiler was replaced by the latest Mk II model at the same time. The fuel consumption had worked out at an average of 0.95 miles/gallon during these 13 months and the consumption of lubricating oil was 0.7 percent of the fuel. BR thus had a very good year's operation at a cost of about £10,000, in place of the usual £30,000 for a Type 4 locomotive.

Following this inspection, the locomotive was then sent to the Eastern Region where it was really worked. It was put onto one of the Deltic diagrams to enable the Deltics to be taken out one at a time for modifications to their train-heating boilers. DP2 was allocated to the Kings Cross No 7 diagram which included the 10.10 Kings Cross to Edinburgh, and the 22.30 Edinburgh to Kings Cross. These were both trains of 450 tons and operating at considerably higher speeds than those worked previously on the LMR. The 10.10 down was then timed at an average of 62.5mph. During this period of deputising for the 3,300hp Deltics, it ran 43,000 miles in 58 days, equivalent to 232,000 miles per annum.

At the end of the summer schedules DP2 went to the Stephenson works at Darlington to be fitted with the stronger type of bogie then being fitted to the Class 37 units on the Western Region, after which it was put to work on the Master Cutler between Kings Cross and Sheffield. This was a waste of a good locomotive, but apart from the Deltic diagrams there was nowhere else it could be used, since all the other diagrams were only suited for the 2,000hp Class 40 units. On one run observed by the author on the Master Cutler only 20 minutes were spent on full load for the whole journey.

In April 1965 it was shown at the exhibition of rolling stock at Marylebone, but on the way there a governor link parted, causing loss of power and it had to be towed from Roade to Willesden. Following this it returned to the Vulcan works for an engine overhaul and tyre-turning as it had completed its 10,000 hours and 380,000 miles. When the engine was stripped down it was found that the pistons were showing signs of overheating; this was thought to be due to the air in the engine room being hotter than desirable due to the ventilation system. Ducts were then installed to the turbocharger intakes from the outside air which was later found to be beneficial to piston life. A new thicker web crankshaft was also installed as the standard for this build of engine.

By this time BR had agreed to rent the locomotive on a permanent basis at a figure of 2/6d [12½p] per mile which on its performance to date would provide a rental of £15,000 per annum, and assuming a normal life, would repay the initial cost of the building.

In January 1966 a set of static control gear was fitted for experimental purposes. In April the turbochargers were reported to be getting excessive dirt deposits on the compressor blades. This was partly due to the change in the air supply system because the airflow rates in the filters supplying the combustion air had been increased by the change in the intake method. The locomotive was also working harder, since more diagrams were becoming available for higher-powered units. A scheme was prepared to equip the turbochargers with water-washing equipment if this trouble persisted.

In September the right-hand leading roller-bearing axlebox on No 1 bogie seized on the main line near Peterborough, and two breakdown cranes had to be sent out to lift the locomotive to enable a replacement bogie to be fitted. In March a joint blew on one of the inlet manifolds and the protective device on the governor operated to cut back the fuel, thus saving a probable piston failure and possibly a complete engine blow-up.

Previously there had been some trouble with the aftercooling system though not serious. As mentioned earlier, in order to reduce weight aluminium tubes had been used in the radiator panels and in the aftercoolers. A mixture of iron and aluminium is not desirable in a cooling system, but this had been accepted and it had proved quite satisfactory. Aftercoolers supplied by both Serck and Marston were on trial, but as a result of various leaks in the panels, which were detected by analysis of the lubricating oil, it was decided to standardise on the Serck type and this change was carried out in April. At the same time the main generator was cleaned and the tyres turned.

DP2 returned to service from Doncaster in May, and on one run recorded in *Railway World* ran from Newcastle to Edinburgh in a net time of 111 minutes, which was three minutes in hand on the time allowance for a Deltic.

On 31 July 1967 DP2, while deputising for a Deltic on the 12 noon from Kings Cross, was involved in an accident near Thirsk on the main line. It hit an overturned cement wagon which had become derailed on an adjacent line, and sustained severe damage to the B side at No 1 end. The main frame and box girders were buckled, but luckily nobody on the locomotive was injured. The mileage at that time was 627,000. DP2 was returned to the Vulcan Foundry and lay there for some time while it was considered whether to rebuild it or not, but by that time BR had plenty of the new Class 47 locomotives in service and did not require this one any more. The engine and generator were removed, rebuilt and sent to Crewe as a spare power unit for the Class 50 fleet. The remainder went for scrap.

Although operationally successful, DP2 was too late to enable English Electric to obtain its share of the 512 locomotives of that power that were ordered, but it did result in an order for 50 of the Class 50 units that were based on DP2. The Class 50s though contained a number of features untried in DP2, which resulted at first in a much poorer performance in service.

BR did very well out of DP2, getting five operational years from a locomotive better than a Type 4 unit at a cost of £80,000 for fuel and hire charges. Maintenance costs during this time would have been very small as no major overhauls were undertaken. To English Electric the cost would would have been around £100,000 allowing for what it received in rental fees. Hardly worth it for 50 locomotives, but it was presumably necessary to show that the firm had closed the gap with Sulzer. Perhaps it has been vindicated by the order for the engines for the Class 56 and Class 58 freight locomotives now in service which use a similar engine.

Another view of DP2 in Eastern Region service, photographed at Finsbury Park in January 1964 with the up Yorkshire Pullman. *British Rail*

CHAPTER SIXTEEN

THE SOUTHERN RAILWAY CO-COS

When the Southern Railway completed the electrification of its main line to Portsmouth on 4 July 1937, this was the third stage in its overall plan for complete main line electrification; the first stages had been to Brighton and other South Coast towns in 1932/5. Operation on these lines had been entirely by multiple-unit passenger stock, but with further electrification planned, attention was given to the operation of freight trains and of through trains from the other railway companies.

Of the four main line railways operating at this time, the Southern had the lowest proportion of freight working, but even so it was quite considerable with 1,000ton coal trains regularly working from the Kent coalfields, and with similar workings to the major South Coast towns. There was a lot of domestic coal used at that time as well as coal for locomotive sheds and factories. There was also special traffic such as boat trains to Dover, Folkestone, Newhaven and Southampton, all of the 400-ton variety and too important in those days to be treated as ordinary multiple-unit stock. These were all included in the planned locomotive operational pattern, which envisaged up to 100 main line electric locomotives.

By 1937 the Southern Railway, which had quietly and systematically proceeded with its third rail electrification scheme, had 610 route miles and 1,550 track miles electrified. It used 520 million units (Kw hr) each year, of which it generated some 30 percent in its own power station at a lower price than those units purchased from other suppliers. The average consumption at the rail was 68 watt/hours per ton mile, and the multiple-unit stock ran 6,000 miles per month, with overhauls of express types at 80,000 miles and suburban ones at 100,000 miles.

Three prototype locomotives were planned by the Southern Railway special development department at London Bridge, and these were to be of the Bo-Bo type with four 375hp traction motors. The mechanical parts were designed by R. E. L. Maunsell in 1936, while the electrical equipment was the responsibility of Alfred Raworth, Chief Electrical Engineer from 1938. Though originally intended to weigh 81 tons, the weight gradually crept up until it reached the limit of 84 tons, when the design was changed to Co-Co.

By the time the design of the Co-Co was undertaken, Bulleid had taken-over as chief mechanical engineer and this work was done at Waterloo with the bogie design being carried out by P. Bolland at Ashford. With a 3-motor bogie there is the problem of providing a suitable pivot due to the presence of the central motor and this is made more difficult within the confines of the UK loading gauge. This can be overcome by the use of a double-bolster bogie with the bolsters between the motors, or as was adopted for the Southern, by the use of a large segmental bearing. It was hoped that design would allow a steadier ride as the bogie centres were only 27½ft apart. This design of bogie was also used on the later Southern diesel-electrics Nos 10201–3 and on the Classes 40, 44, 45 and 46 built by BR and English Electric.

It had been intended to articulate the bogies and

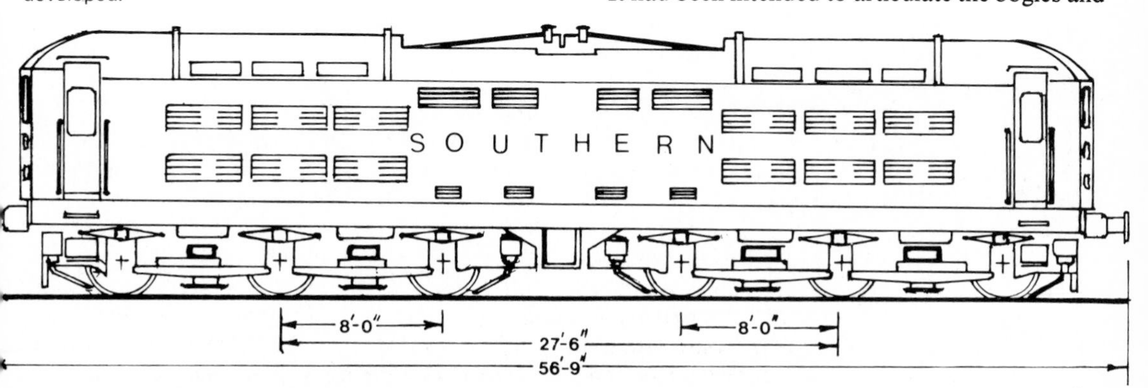

Drawing of the 1,470hp Co-Co electric locomotive as developed.

to mount the buffers and drawgear on them, but in the final design the drawgear was attached to the main frame. The bogies were initially articulated, but as this was too stiff and gave poor ride control this feature was soon removed.

Although there were four collector shoes each side there would be occasions when the whole locomotives would be out of contact with the live rail; in order to maintain tractive effort over these gaps, two motor generator booster sets were provided, each with a 1-ton flywheel running at 1,800rpm. This was the first time this feature had been tried in the UK as previous electric locomotives had relied on the skill of the driver so as not to get stuck on a gap. The two shoebeams on each side of each bogie had a flexible mounting at each end and were covered in plywood for the safety of staff when operating in sidings.

It had also been anticipated that with extensive freight working, some sidings would be provided with overhead current supply for safety reasons and a central pantograph was fitted to permit this type of operation. A short length of siding to the north of Balcombe tunnel on the Brighton line was equipped with an overhead line – trials and demonstrations were carried out there, but that was the only use ever made of this feature.

The design specification of this first locomotive, No CC1, was 1,470hp as a 1-hour rating, using six English Electric 519A traction motors with fan cooling at a supply voltage of 660Vdc. The specification called for the haulage of 1,000-ton freight trains, and for 425-ton passenger trains at up to 75mph (the civil engineer's limit) with a balancing speed on level track of 60mph, the same as the express multiple-unit stock.

Each booster set was electrically coupled to the bogie underneath and arranged so that either set could be cut out in the event of a severe fault, and the locomotive worked at half power on the other set of motors. The controller had 26 notches, and for the first 16 of these, the booster output opposed the line voltage, gradually increasing this across the three motors from zero to 660V. After this the next seven notches boosted the output to twice the line voltage thus increasing the motor voltage to 440V across each; the last three notches brought in weak field operation.

The chassis consisted of four I frames running the full length between the buffers. The box-shaped body, with rounded ends and roofs, housed the two driver's cabs, two booster sets, two control frames, two Northey rotary exhausters for passenger train braking, an electric train-heating boiler to supply 1,040 lb steam per hour at 50 lb/sq in with a water tank capacity of 330 gallons, as well as a motor generator set for battery charging and a set of Ni-Fe batteries for traction boost purposes. Below the underframe between the bogies were two Westinghouse compressors as fitted on the multiple-unit stock to supply air for the locomotive brakes at 90 lb/sq in as well as for the control gear and sanding.

The overall length was 56ft 9in with a width of 8ft 6in so that the locomotive could eventually operate on the restricted Hastings line through the narrow tunnels at Somerhill, Mountfield and Strawberry Hill. The first two sets of mechanical parts were completed at Ashford and towed to Brighton where the English Electric electrical equipment was fitted, No CC1 being finished in July 1941. The final weight came out at 99.7 tons. The starting tractive effort was 40,000 lb falling to 11,130 lb at 35mph.

When working passenger stock the braking was operated by the train valve with a proportional valve for the locomotive brakes, but when working loose-coupled freight stock, the locomotive brakes only were used. This posed a problem for emergency braking in the event of the dead man's control becoming operational through driver error or collapse. If the emergency brake came on fully the effect on the guard's van at the other end of the train could have been disastrous, even fatal, for the guard, and in any case a derailment would have been highly probable anywhere along the train. This was overcome by an initial application at 8 lb/sq in for 35 seconds to enable the train to buffer-up, after which the full brake application was made.

During 1941 tests were carried out between Selhurst and Brighton with passenger trains of 14 coaches and with 1,000-ton freight trains, to test the overall performance and to check the acceleration and braking. The accelerating current was steady at 800A up to 37mph, and the rates of acceleration were 0.5mph/second with 425-ton passenger trains, and 0.3mph/second with the 1,000-ton freight train. The balancing speed on the level with the 425-ton train was 65mph.

During these trials and in subsequent operational service, a number of problems came to light, and, although there were sometimes technical staff on the locomotive, there were many occasions when fault descriptions had to be given by drivers unfamiliar with this sort of equipment.

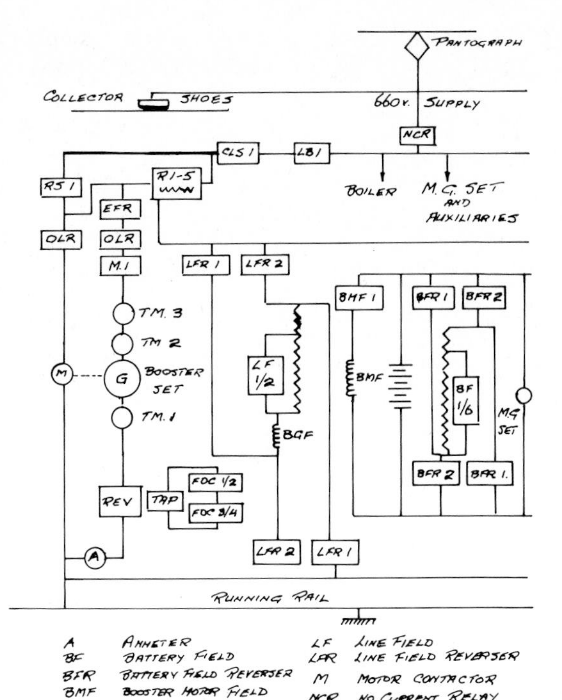

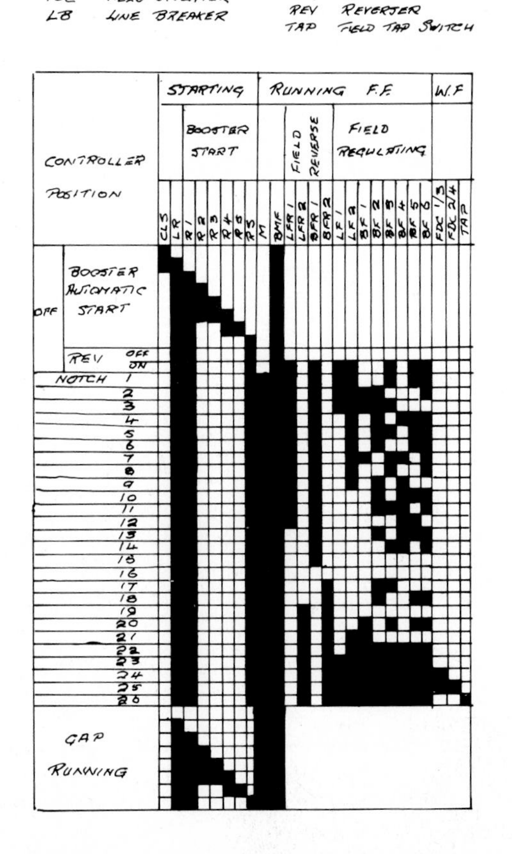

This coupled with the refusal of faults to repeat themselves did not always help the solution of these problems.

The first problem was with flashovers on the booster motors due to short circuits on the live rail caused by hanging brake pins or other portions of freight stock. The rate of current rise was found to be of the order of ten million amps per second, requiring a circuit-breaker opening speed of 0.0035sec. Tests on the London Transport at this time had shown voltage surges up to 15,000V due to this problem of short circuits on the live rail. The actual time response of the overload circuit breaker was 0.2 sec which was obviously much too slow, and the solution was found in a Branchu type of current limiting relay which was used in distribution switchgear. This limiter (CLS in the circuit diagram) fitted in each booster motor circuit operated on the rate of current increase and interposed a resistance to limit the current to 1,600A. The potential drop across this resistance operated the line breaker (LB). This limiter had a primary winding and a single turn secondary coil which operated a bucking bar, thus inserting a limited resistance and created a powerful flux in the breaker air gap. A speed of operation of 0.0023sec was achieved, which gave the required protection. The limiter was bridged-out in the first two starting notches as shown in the sequence chart.

It was also found that if the locomotive ran onto a supposedly dead section of the conductor rail, the booster motor voltage could energise the conductor rail, thus providing a danger to the permanent way staff working in that area. This was overcome by means of a differential relay which detected line and booster motor voltages and ensured that the line breaker (LB) was always open unless the line voltage was 15 percent greater than the motor back electromotive force.

From the time that No CC1 came out in 1941, the Southern Railway had been very busy with wartime traffic, and trying to cope with bombing and troop movements; this coupled with material shortages meant that the second locomotive, No CC2, was not completed until 1945. This was basically similar to CC1, but had a horizontal controller.

(*Top*) Power circuit diagram for Southern Railway electric Co-Co locomotive No CC1.

(*Left*) Sequence operating chart for No CC1.

The third version, No 20003, was completed in 1948 and this had quite a few differences from the other two. The flywheels in the booster sets were increased in size by 200lb and the 1-hour rating to 1,560hp by the use of EE519/4D motors. The top speed was also increased to 85mph. The armatures in these motors were wedge-locked and not banded as in the former type. No 20003 was increased in length by 1ft 6in to allow extra water capacity for the train-heating boiler. It is not known why this was done since the earlier two locomotives had apparently not operated passenger trains.

The overall length came to 58ft 3in with 28ft 6in between bogie centres. This one, unlike the other two, was equipped with square-end cabs, reputedly to match the Leader class being produced at Brighton at that time. In No 20003 the controller was operated by a wheel, and the driver could go straight to weak field, whereas in the former two he had to revert to zero before using this feature.

From 15 May 1949 regular working commenced on the boat trains between Victoria and Newhaven Harbour, and a typical weekday roster for the three units in 1954 is shown in Table 8. This shows a daily mileage of between 334 and 431 miles, and the average annual mileage was between 70,000 and 80,000. When used on freight service, the locomotives were limited to a maximum of 35mph if hauling grease-lubricated wagons – fine for the locomotives, but not so good for the wagons, which were very prone to hot boxes at that speed!

No 20003 at Victoria with Newhaven boat train. This third locomotive differed from the other two, as is evidenced in this illustration. *W. Philip Conolly*

The worst operating problem was that of the train-heating equipment, largely due to poor water. The elements were protected by quartz tubes and the hardness deposits caused these to crack. It was this experience which led the Southern Region to insist on electric heating on its new diesel locomotives and multiple-unit diesel-electric stock when it received these under the modernisation scheme.

One incident that was typical of the co-operation between the equipment suppliers, English Electric, and the Southern, occurred when one of the control frames was burned-out on a

The prototype, as BR No 20001, just west of Clapham Junction with the 09.30 Victoria–Newhaven boat train on 5 July 1964. *Brian Stephenson*

Monday due to careless maintenance. That night the frame was removed and put on to a lorry that had come from Preston. The frame arrived at Preston on the Tuesday evening, was completely rebuilt by Thursday and returned to Brighton that night. The frame was refitted and the locomotive returned to traffic that week-end. This sort of co-operation paid off in the subsequent supply of electric and diesel-electric traction equipment to the Southern Region, all of which, except for the Class 33 locomotives, is of English Electric (now GEC) manufacture.

The lessons learned in these three prototype locomotives were designed into the 2,550 hp Bo-Bo units with booster sets produced in 1959, which only weighed 77 tons and gave a tractive effort of 43,000lb. 24 of these Class 71 were built, ten of which were later converted to the Class 74 electro-diesels. All of these have now been withdrawn.

Under the BR numbering scheme Nos CC1 and CC2 became 20001 and 20002, joining No 20003 which carried its BR number from the start. They were withdrawn in 1968. The original CC1 probably achieved 1.5 million miles during its life. Had the 1939/45 war not interrupted the Southern's planned electrification there would have been many more of these very successful locomotives in service.

Table 8

Weekday Rosters for Southern Region Electric Locomotives Class 7P/5F Nos 20001–3, 1954

DIAGRAM No 1

Arrive		*Depart*
–	Newhaven Harbour	06.10
07.20	Victoria	09.31
10.43	Newhaven	11.38
12.31	Three Bridges	14.38
15.25	Lewes	15.26
15.36	Newhaven	17.15
18.28	Victoria	20.20
21.30	Newhaven	21.57
23.22	New Cross Gate	00.09
02.00	Lewes	03.00
03.50	Three Bridges	04.05
04.43	Newhaven Harbour	–

DIAGRAM No 2

Arrive		*Depart*
–	Horsham	05.45
07.04	Norwood	07.48
11.25	Polegate	11.40
12.45	Haywards Heath	13.03
13.40	Hove	15.20
16.20	Chichester	16.48
18.12	Horsham	20.16
21.40	Chichester	21.58
01.12	Norwood	01.45
02.59	Horsham	–

DIAGRAM No 3

Arrive		*Depart*
–	Chichester	10.58
11.56	Hove	12.36
13.15	Three Bridges	13.25
14.00	Horsham	14.30
14.50	Three Bridges	15.10
15.27	Horsham	15.39
16.53	Chichester	17.25
19.52	Worthing	20.16
20.48	Chichester	21.10
22.56	Three Bridges	22.57
23.45	Horsham	00.55
03.26	Fratton	03.45
04.08	Chichester	–

CHAPTER SEVENTEEN

THE GAS TURBINE TRIO – NEARLY A QUARTET

No. 18000

British Railways and in particular the Western Region did give the gas turbine prime mover a fair trial, but like earlier steam turbine applications it was not to prove successful.

The first tested was a 2,500hp A1A-A1A unit, No 18000, supplied by Brown Boveri of Baden and SLM of Winterthur. This was the result of a visit paid by F. W. Hawksworth in 1945 to study a 2,000hp gas turbine locomotive then in service on the Swiss Federal Railways.

The Brown Boveri turbine design consisted of a single-shaft machine driven by a turbine having seven rows of reaction blading giving 10,300hp at 5,300rpm. This drove the generator through a 19-stage axial compressor absorbing 7,800hp, and then through a reduction gearbox with a ratio of 6.6/1. The compressor delivered air at a compression ratio of 3.2/1 through a heat exchanger, fed by the turbine exhaust, to a separate combustion chamber as shown below.

The combustion chamber was designed to operate on class F fuel (950 seconds Redwood at 100°F) with a calorific value of 17,400 BTU per lb, giving an inlet temperature to the turbine of 1,100°F. The exhaust temperature was designed to be 480°F and the air consumption at full load was 44,300cu ft/minute (1.5 tons).

A Saurer engine drove a 40kW 110V dc generator for the auxiliary supplies, and a train-heating boiler with an output of 1,000 lb of steam per hour was installed next to one of the driving cabs; the control cubicle was next to the cab at the other end. The two SLM bogies each had two traction motors of 397kW at 1,550rpm, with driving wheels of 4ft 0in diameter. The whole locomotive was 63ft long overall and weighed 119.2 tons, with a maximum axle load of 20.6 tons. The cost was around £138,000.

After a few runs in Switzerland it arrived via Harwich and was towed to Swindon on 5 February 1950, first running under power from Swindon to Badminton on the 13 February. After some adjustment runs and driver training, it hauled a test train of 436 tons over the 78.6 miles between Plymouth and Taunton in 109 minutes with a fuel consumption of 32.8 lb per mile and an overall drawbar efficiency of 6.45 percent.

It operated its first passenger train from Paddington to Swindon 19 May, but before this a compressor blade had failed on 9 March when working empty stock to Bristol. This failure was attributed to flutter caused by water washing nozzles which had been installed for blade cleaning. This was overcome by a blade lacing ring.

Diagram of Brown Boveri gas turbine locomotive No 18000.

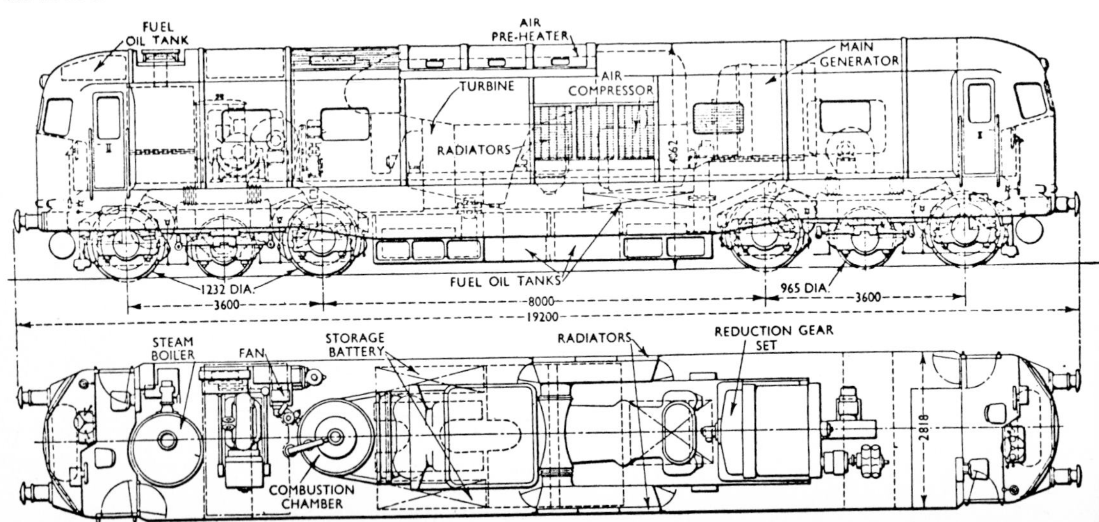

After a week in service between Paddington and Swindon it operated between Paddington and Plymouth from 22 May hauling the 15.30 from Paddington and returning on the 07.15 from Plymouth, putting in up to 460 miles a day.

In June a new lining was required for the combustion chamber, following which tests were carried out on 12 June on the gradient from Plymouth to Hermerdon. A previous test had shown that a 436 tons trailing load could be taken up the 1 in 42 gradient without stopping, and that 290 tons could be started from rest on that gradient. This corresponded to the maker's performance figures, but the traffic department requested a trial with two extra coaches making 350 tons, and the result was a damaged traction motor.

It took a long time to convince the operating folk that locomotive manufacturers' figures were genuine and that for electric motors these could be accurately worked out. Later thousands of hours and much money was to be spent on unnecessary tests and trials to prove this point.

Following this motor failure the locomotive ran on three motors until the repaired motor was installed again. It then ran fairly regularly to Plymouth and back until October when attention was needed to the train-heating boiler, keeping it out of service until January 1951. During this first year it ran 23,200 miles with stoppages due to leaking fuel tanks and minor electrical faults, but principally the train-heating boiler.

During the next year it worked first between Paddington and Swindon and then on to Bristol, running 2,200 miles a week until June; then a serious fire in the heat exchanger, caused by accumulation of soot, put it out of service until mid-August. After repair it undertook further dynamometer car trials between London and Plymouth and then reverted to service on the Bristol run. By the end of the second year it had run 72,600 miles.

The dynamometer car trials in September 1951 entailed pulling 395 tons to Westbury, 359 tons to Exeter and 239 tons thence to Plymouth. The 225 miles were run in 252 minutes, with stops at Taunton and Exeter against a booked time of 259 minutes, with a fuel consumption of 5,318 lb of oil. Comparable runs with Castle class No 5049 and King class No 6022 gave coal consumptions of 8,030 lb and 7,920 lb respectively. Overall efficiencies worked out at:

No 18000 leaving Paddington on the 15.30 West of England express in 1948. *F. R. Hebron/Rail Archive Stephenson*

Gas turbine No 18000	6.6 percent
Castle No 5049	5.45 percent
King class No 6022	5.36 percent

These results were disappointing because the full load efficiency of the gas turbine unit on test had been 16.9 percent, but the gas turbine efficiency falls away sharply below 0.8 load, and with so much power in hand most of the rail traction work was inevitably at part load. This was the main weakness with all the gas turbine units.

Other results from the dynamometer car tests gave a starting tractive effort of 30,000 lb up to 20mph, falling to 8,800 lb at 70mph, and to 4,500 lb at 85mph. The locomotive resistance varied from 5 lb per ton at 30mph, to 16 lb per ton at 85mph, and balancing speeds on level track were:

Train weight (tons)	*Speed (mph)*
300	82.7
400	78.0
500	74.6
600	71.7

The uphill performance was noticeably better than that of a King class, the climb to Whiteball from Exeter being 18mph to 20mph faster than the King, with similar results on other grades. The steady drawbar horsepower of 2,065hp from 35mph to 58mph was obviously better than the steam locomotive could give for long periods.

In September some cracks in the first and second rows of the turbine blades probably caused by delayed ignition, resulted in a further withdrawal, but by the end of the third year a total of 122,120 miles had been registered, with 3,296 hours of turbine operation. Since this turbine had been designed to run on 950 second fuel, the running was confined to locations where this fuel (which had to be heated in storage) was obtainable. As the only depots where this could be done were Old Oak Common (London), Swindon, and Laira (Plymouth) the operation was confined to the London-Bristol and London-Plymouth routes, rather as the former GWR Pacific No 111 *The Great Bear* had been confined to the former.

There were perennial problems with the train-heating boiler and with the combustion chamber, though thicker ones made of titanium alloy improved this, but this item generally needed changing twice a year.

No 18000 ran for a further three years, achieving around 400,000 miles, until another traction motor failure caused its withdrawal. It was then transferred to the Rugby Locomotive Testing Station to act as a power supply vehicle and was returned to Swindon in 1960. In January 1965 it was towed to Harwich by Brush locomotive No D5666 and returned to Brown Boveri in Switzerland. In July 1965 it was transferred to the Swiss Federal Railways, which converted it into a mobile laboratory for use by the UIC office of research and experiments. The gas turbine was removed and one new bogie fitted, with its central axle driven by an Alsthom TAO646 traction motor. It is officially known as 'Test Machine 18000', but carries the unofficial name *Elizabetta*.

No 18100

The second gas turbine locomotive, No 18100, was built by Metropolitan Vickers Ltd and delivered to Swindon in December 1951. This was a Co-Co design with a potential output of 3,500hp at 7,000rpm. The turbine output was 10,000hp with the compressor absorbing 6,500hp, leaving 3,500hp available on the output shaft. This was coupled through a 4.37 to 1 reduction gear to three main generators with one auxiliary set and one exciter. Each main generator was a 6-pole dc machine with an output of 1100A at 660V running at 1,600rpm and feeding two traction motors. Each traction motor took 550A and could run up to 1,900rpm, which with a gear ratio of 2.76 to 1 and 3ft 8in driving wheels, gave a top speed of 90mph. With a driving cab at each end and a train-heating boiler with an output of 1,500lb of steam per hour, the overall length came to 66ft 9in and the total weight to 130 tons 2cwt; the maximum axle load was 22 tons.

Driver's control desk on No 18000.

The gas turbine was intended for operation only on gas oil, and the main tank had a capacity of 995 gallons. The engine efficiency on test was 20 percent at full load and 16.5 percent at half load. The cost was stated to be around £170,000.

This gas turbine was a single-shaft machine like the Brown Boveri, but there were six combustion chambers arranged around the turbine, with no heat exchanger; being of the aircraft type it was designed to run only on gas oil having a calorific value of 19,500 BTU/lb. The turbine had five rows of blades and was designed for an inlet temperature of 1,300°F. It drove through a 15-stage axial compressor having a pressure ratio of 5.25 to 1 and thence through the reduction gear to the generators. The turbine speed was 7,000rpm and the air consumption was 40,000cu ft/min (1.35 tons).

Following running in tests and driver training, a train of 532 tons was worked from Swindon to Plymouth on 6 March 1952, and on 9 March, a train of 609 tons was started from rest on the 1 in 42 gradient at Hemerdon. Regular passenger operation was commenced in April and No 18100 worked between London and Bristol as well as London to Plymouth until September, when a fire in the control cubicle caused its withdrawal for rewiring. By then it had achieved 42,000 miles in just over six months, a creditable performance.

The initial fuel consumption had been high at 3.77 gallons per mile, but by adjustment to the idling control this was brought down to 2.97 gallons per mile (still about three times that of an equivalent diesel locomotive). Operation was continued without much enthusiasm for the next five years until the arrival of the diesel-hydraulic

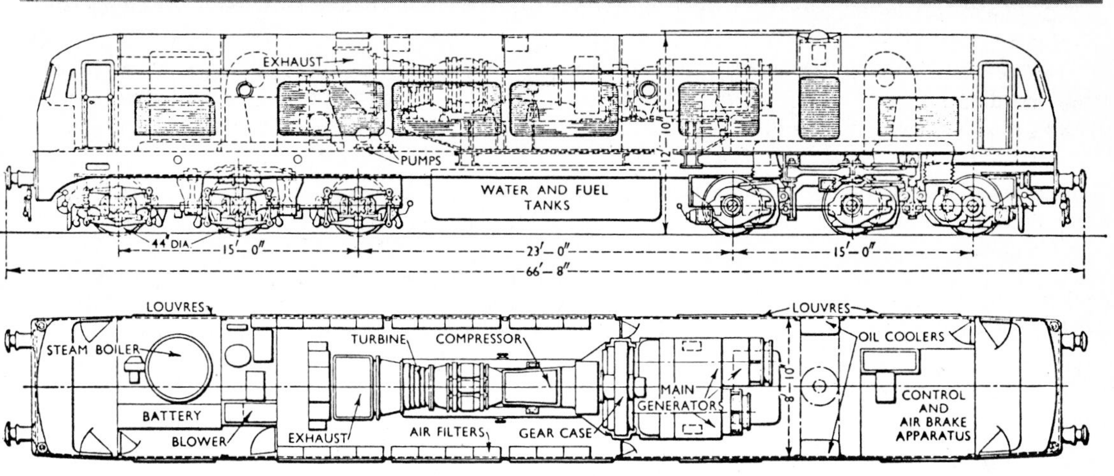

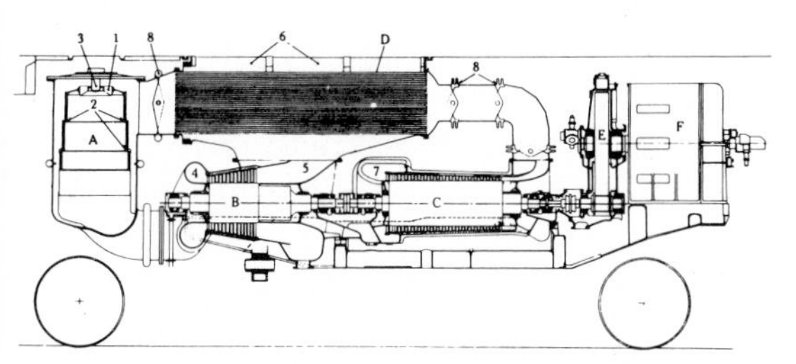

The completed No 18100 at Trafford Park.

Diagram of Metropolitan Vickers gas turbine locomotive No 18100.

Cross-section of gas turbine power unit.

locomotives, when further trials of this unit were not considered necessary.

After withdrawal in 1958, when it had run for some 250,000 miles, it was returned to Metropolitan Vickers at Trafford Park and rebuilt as an A1A-A1A electric locomotive, numbered first E1001 and later E2001. In this form it was used for driver training on the 25kV electrified lines between Crewe and Manchester, mainly on the Styal loop until the arrival of the AEI/BRCW Bo-Bo electrics Nos E3001-23 (later Class 81) in 1959.

Both Nos 18000 and 18100 performed well in service, but their superior power could not be used fully since fleet operation is necessary in order to utilise higher-powered units to their full advantage as was done in the case of the Class 55 Deltics. In fact, it counted against them in that so much of their work had to be at part load, which is the worst method of using a gas turbine.

It was said that they acted as vacuum cleaners for all the stations and tunnels they passed through and removed most of the 120 years' accumulation of steam locomotive soot, which must have been to the benefit of the ensuing diesels on the Western Region. Their maintenance costs were reasonably low, and if their fuel consumption had not been so high they could have proved most effective traction units.

GT3

Apart from the Fell, GT3 was the only main line locomotive to be designed with mechanical drive to the wheels, and the only one of the gas turbine trio to adopt this system. In some ways it was almost a political animal, being the last defiant gesture of the steam folk at the Vulcan Foundry Newton-le-Willows against their electrical masters, the English Electric Traction Division at Bradford. It took so long in the gestation period that it was out-of-date by the time it appeared on rails.

The English Electric Willans works at Rugby had for long been producing steam turbines, and naturally got into the gas turbine business as soon as possible. By 1947 its EM27 industrial set was designed to produce 2,700hp, and when British Rail showed interest in gas turbine locomotives the design for GT3 was started. Since the predominant locomotives at that time were the conventional steam types it was thought that a layout on their lines would appeal to British Railways. There was no shortage of turntables at that time and the problems of one driving position only were not considered serious.

The appeal of the mechanical drive in order to eliminate the losses in an electrical transmission overlooked the loss resulting from low output shaft speeds at other than the top output speed. As the turbine can only run in one direction the gearbox needed a reversing mechanism with safety interlocks to ensure that the gear direction could not be changed unless the locomotive were at rest; in neutral the turbine output shaft was held stationary by a brake in the driver's cab. The secondary output shaft was connected through a reduction gearbox having a ratio of 20.51 to 1, and the final drive was flexible to allow for the normal misalignment due to rolling and rail movements. The output was delivered to the centre axle of a 4–6–0 wheel arrangement.

The EM27 turbine was a 2-shaft machine, one shaft driving the compressor, the other supplying the power output. The maximum measured output of the turbine was 19,800hp, of which the compressor absorbed 17,100hp, leaving 2,700hp available as output. The designed turbine speed was 8,250rpm for the primary high-pressure turbine and 9,000rpm for the low-pressure turbine.

The combustion air was drawn in at the front end of the locomotive through 64 dry fabric filters and passed to the compressor. From the compressor the air passed to a heat-exchanger and thence to the combustion chamber, after which it went to the high-pressure and low-pressure turbines, and finally to exhaust through the heat-exchanger. An oil tank holding 350 gallons was mounted just in front of the driver's cab, while a conventional-shaped tender held the train heating boiler, a 2,000-gallon fuel tank, and a water tank for the boiler, containing 1,400 gallons. The overall weight for the locomotive was 79tons 8cwt tons, with 44 tons for the tender. The maximum load on the driving axles was 19 tons 14 cwt.

Auxiliaries consisted of a vacuum brake ejector operated by compressed air from the main compressor, and a dc generator drive from the primary shaft to charge a set of batteries. These batteries provided the drive for the main lubricating oil pump and for the starting motor. Starting took 100 seconds and propane gas was used initially to ignite the oil burners. The battery capacity had to be adequate to keep the oil pump running after shut-down to maintain the flow of oil to the turbine bearings to avoid shaft distortion.

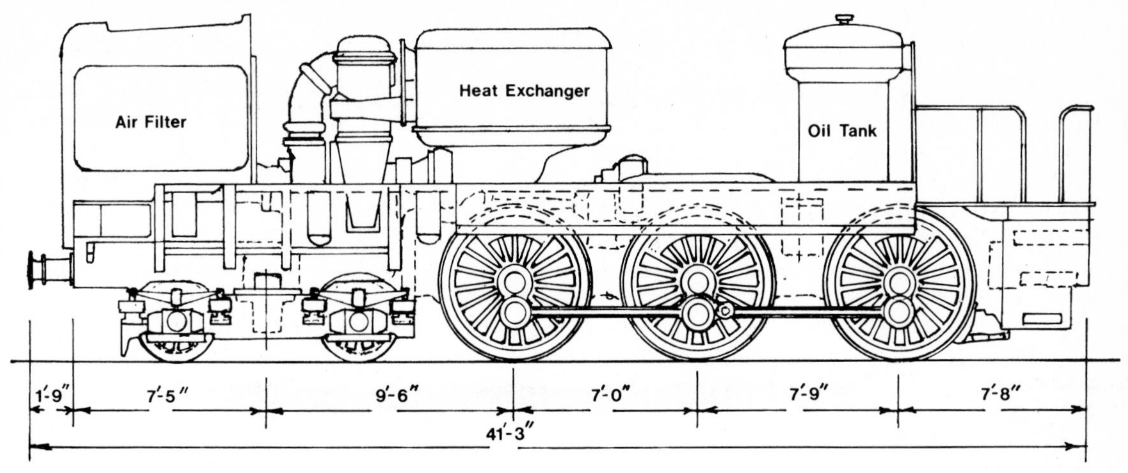

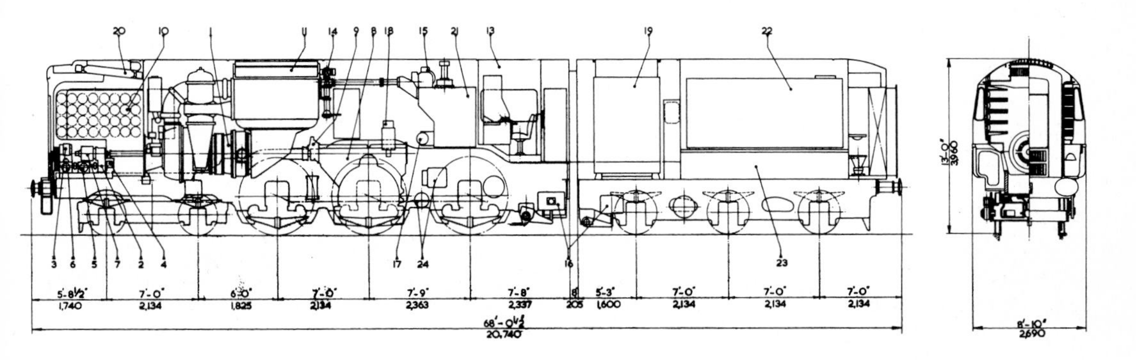

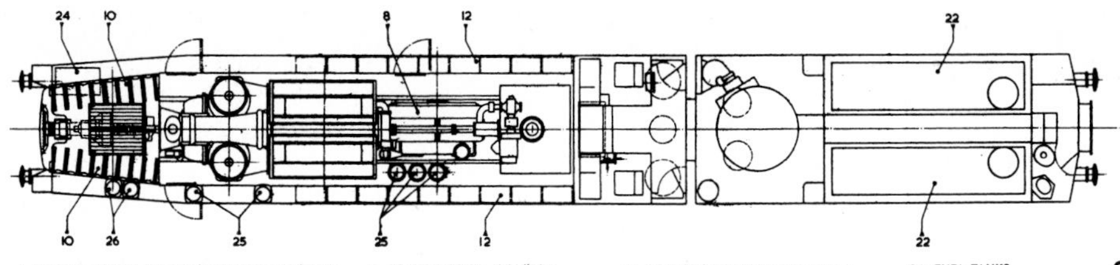

1 ENGINE - EM 27L RECUPERATIVE GAS TURBINE.
2 ENGINE DRIVEN AUXILIARIES GEARBOX.
3 ALTERNATOR.
4 FUEL PUMP.
5 LUBRICATING OIL PRESSURE PUMP.
6 LUBRICATING OIL SCAVENGE PUMP.
7 STARTER MOTOR.
8 TRANSMISSION GEARBOX.
9 POWER TURBINE BALANCE GEAR.
10 AIR INTAKE FILTER.
11 EXHAUST CHIMNEY.
12 BATTERIES.
13 DRIVING CAB.
14 VACUUM BRAKE EJECTOR.
15 AIR MOTOR DRIVEN EXHAUSTER.
16 BRAKE CYLINDERS.
17 ELECTRIC DRIVEN PUMP SET.
18 ELECTRIC DRIVEN COOLING PUMP SET.
19 TRAIN HEATING BOILER.
20 OIL COOLER.
21 OIL TANK.
22 FUEL TANKS.
23 WATER TANK.
24 OIL SUCTION FILTER.
25 OIL PRESSURE FILTER.
26 FUEL OIL FILTER.

GENERAL LAYOUT OF 2700 HP. GAS TURBINE LOCOMOTIVE TYPE 4-6-0

(*Top*) Diagram of 4–6–0 gas turbine NO GT3 as tested at Rugby.

(*Above*) General layout of 2,700hp 4–6–0 gas turbine locomotive No GT3.

GT3 was assembled at the Vulcan Foundry and towed to the locomotive testing station at Rugby in February 1959, after some 12 years in design and assembly. Even then it was only in semi-finished condition with no outer casing or tender, and a Shell-BP oil tank wagon was used for the fuel supplies. A special towing pump was fitted to supply oil to the gears and bearings when the locomotive was being towed.

The first problem on test was with the lubricating system, and it was found that with a common lubricant the oil was too heavy for the turbine bearings and too light for the final gears. The oil was pumped from the bottom of the gear casing through a cooler and back to the main tank where de-aeration took place in the upper portion of the tank. This scavenge pump could not keep the oil level below that of the gearing, resulting in oil being forced through the axle seals. The suction pipe was lowered and the gear casing sump was enlarged to overcome this trouble.

Other problems with the lubrication system included a failure to de-aerate when power was applied rapidly, though the control was designed to prevent too rapid an increase in the fuel rate, as this could cause surging in the compressor. A by-pass also had to be fitted to the oil cooler to overcome excess pressure when starting with cold oil, as this tended to burst the flexible hoses.

The next problem was a major one and was caused by the fouling of the turbine rotor blade tips on the stator casing. This had not occurred in other EM27 turbines and was probably due to the nature of the load, since the output shaft had to start from stationary against full load, which does not occur in electrical generation or marine propulsion. Being an early design of turbine, the blades did not have air-cooling holes, thus causing heat distortion. The blade tips had to be shortened, and after this the maximum speed was reduced to 7,700rpm, reducing the output to 2,190hp and the wheel rim output to just under 2,000hp.

Before the trouble with the turbine blades and when the full output was available, the test results showed a maximum output of 2,420hp at the wheel rim at 55mph; at this output the fuel consumption was 1,600 lb per hour or 0.66 lb per horsepower hour. At half load corresponding to 45mph, the fuel rate was 1,130 lb per hour or 0.94 lb per horsepower hour, while at quarter load the fuel rate was 700 lb per hour or 1.16 lb per horsepower hour. (The diesel equivalents at these rates would have been 0.5 at full load, 0.5 at half load and 0.6 at quarter load).

Subsequent to the shortening of the turbine blades and the reduction in output these figures came to:

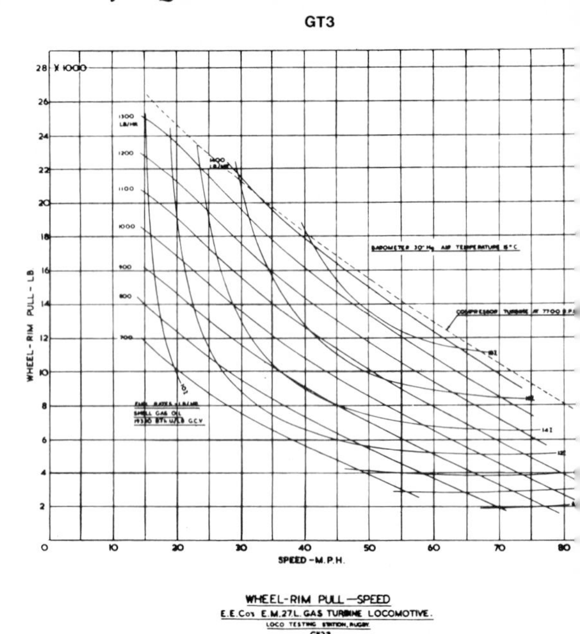

0.7 lb per horsepower hour at full load (55mph)
0.95 lb per horsepower hour at half load (40mph)
1.33 lb per horsepower hour at quarter load (35mph)

The maximum tractive effort was stated to be 38,000 lb, but the highest measured on test was 25,000 lb at 15mph. GT3 was later tested with two 2–8–0 freight locomotives, which it started from rest on a 1 in 44 gradient, but the start was very slow until the output turbine was able to build up some speed.

Following these tests at Rugby GT3 returned to Vulcan Foundry where it was completed and it was exhibited at the 50th anniversary of the Institution of Locomotive Engineers at Marylebone on 4 February 1961. During 1961 it carried out some local testing with small trains out of Crewe, and in December was scheduled to carry out some dynamometer car trials between Crewe and Carlisle over Shap, hauling a load of 466 tons.

The first test on 13 December had to be cancelled due to flat batteries, but on 14 December the running soon showed a severe power shortage, and it was over one hour late on arrival at Carlisle. The drawbar measurements that were to have been taken had to be abandoned and the ascent to Shap carried out at the maximum speed possible; this proved to be 20mph on the 1 in 75 grade instead of the 38mph calculated. Downhill coasting tests to

GT3 nearing completion.

4–6–0 gas turbine locomotive No GT3 passing Shap Summit during trials between Crewe and Carlisle. *English Electric Co. Ltd.*

ascertain the locomotive resistance also had to be abandoned since the driver dropped the compressor speed below the safe rate of 2,700rpm and the stop button had to be used and the train brought to rest.

On the return a fire started in the cab due to overheating of the starter for the lubricating oil pump, which delayed the departure, and in order to prevent a recurrence of the low speed problem with the compressor, the rate was kept at 6,000rpm and the control carried out by the locomotive brakes. Finally the train could not be started on the 1 in 131 gradient at Upperby Bridge and banking assistance was needed.

Drawbar tractive effort readings were 20,900 lb up to 10mph, and 12,500 lb at 50mph, equivalent to 1,627hp. Since the locomotive would require around 245hp at that speed and the transmission losses were estimated at 170hp, this would correspond to a turbine output of 2,042hp.

In view of the unreliability of the output and the fact that the design was out-of-date by 1961 – turntables were rapidly being abolished – no further tests were justified, and GT3 was withdrawn. The turbine was returned to Rugby where it was made, and the rest went to a firm at Salford for scrap. The total mileage achieved, including some 5,000 miles while at the Rugby testing station, was 17,200 miles.

"The one that might have been . . ."

Finally, a brief mention might be made of the 'gas turbine that never was.' This was to have been a coal-fired C-C design and was sponsored by the Ministry of Fuel & Power. The turbine was to have been developed and built by C. A. Parsons & Co Ltd, and the rest by the North British Locomotive Co Ltd.

In order to prevent the ash in the combustion products passing through the turbine, a heat exchanger was proposed to heat the air before entry to the turbines. These were to be of the 2-shaft type, with the output shaft driving to both bogies through a gearbox and cardan shafts.

Work was started in 1951 and the designers hoped for an efficiency as high as 19 percent at full load, but the Modernisation Plan prevented it coming to fruition. In view of the troubles with gearboxes and cardan shafts, it was perhaps lucky for all concerned that it was never built.

If and when the world's oil runs out, something like this might have to be revived.

APPENDIX 1

SUMMARY OF DETAILS OF THE PROTOTYPE LOCOMOTIVES

Steam locomotives

Loco-motive number	*Built*	*Builder*	*Drawbar Horse-power*	*Wheel arrange-ment*	*Weight (tons)*	*Axle load (tons)*	*Max speed (mph)*	*Boiler*	
								pressure lb/sq in	*heating area (sq ft)*
20	1902	GER	–	0–10–0	78.5	16.7	30	200	3,010
40	1906	GWR	1,100	4–4–2	75.0	19.0	90	225	2,142
2299	1911	MR	–	2–6–2	80.0	18.7	82	180	2,170
23141	1924	NBL	1,000	4–4–4–4	–		50	170	
160	1922	AW	1,200	2–6–6–2	150.2	24.0	59	200	
6233	1926	BP	2,000	10–6–4	143.7	18.0	76	300	2,260
–	1928	Kitson	800	2–6–2	70.0	17.0	45	180	1,071
10000	1929	LNER	1,560	4–6–4	103.6	21.6	60	400	2,126
6399	1929	NBL	–	4–6–0	89.5	23.6	50	1,800	
						21.8			
6202	1935	LMS	2,400	4–6–2	110.5		85	250	2,168
36001	1949	SR	–	C–C	131.0		65	280	

Diesel locomotives

Loco-motive number	*Built*	*Builder*	*Brake horse-power*	*Wheel arrange-ment*	*Weight (tons)*	*Axle load (tons)*	*Max speed (mph)*	*Engine*
10000	1947	LMS	1,600	Co-Co	127.6	21.2	85	EE Co 16SVT
10001	1948	LMR	1,600	Co-Co	127.6	21.2	85	EE Co 16SVT
10800	1950	NBL	800	Bo-Bo	69.8	17.5	70	Paxman 16RPH
10100	1950	LMR	2,300	2–D–2	123.5	19.0	78	4 Paxman 12RP
10201	1950	BR(SR)	1,760	1Co-Co1	135.0	18.5	110	EE Co 16SVT
10202	1951	BR(SR)	1,760	1Co-Co1	135.0	18.5	110	EE Co 16SVT
10203	1954	BR(SR)	2,000	1Co-Co1	132.0	18.6	90	EE Co 16SVT MkII
Deltic	1955	EE Co	3,300	Co-Co	106.0	17.6	105	2 Napier 18–25
D0226	1957	EE Co	500	C	48.0	16.0	60	EE Co 6RKT
D0227	1957	EE Co	500	C	48.0	16.0	60	EE Co 6RKT
D0280	1961	Brush	2,800	Co-Co	115.5	19.3	100	2 Maybach MD
D0260	1962	BRCW	2,750	Co-Co	114.0	19.0	100	Sulzer 12LDA
DP2	1962	EE Co	2,700	Co-Co	105.0	17.5	105	EE Co 16CSVT
D5835	1962	Brush	2,000	A1A–A1A	106.0	19.0	90	MBD 12JVSST
HS4000	1968	Brush	4,000	Co-Co	126.0	21.0	125	Sulzer 16LVA
47 061	1976	BREL	3,250	Co-Co				EE Co 16CRK3T
47 901	1978	BREL	3,250	Co-Co				EE Co 12CRK3T

Appendix

Cylinders No.	Dia (in)	Stroke (in)	Driving wheel diameter (in)	Tractive effort (lb)	Withdrawn	Mileage	Notes
3	18.5	24.0	54	38,000	1913	200	Rebuilt as 0–8–0
4	15.0	26.0	80	27,800	1957	2,000,000	Converted to Castle Class 4–6–0
8	18.0	12.0	64	28,600	1912	200	
	Turbine		48	16,000	1927	200	
	Turbine				1924	100	Overweight
	Turbine		63	40,300	1928	20,000	
8	13.5	15.5	60	25,450	1933	1,000	Still diesel/steam axle
2	10.0	26.0		32,000	1959	90,000	Converted to W1 No 10000,
2	20.0	26.0	80				BR No 60700
1	11.5	26.0		33,200	1933	400	Converted to LMS No 6170
2	18.0	26.0	80				*British Legion*
	Turbine		80	40,000	1952	420,000	Written-off in Harrow accident, 1952
6	12.25	16.0	61	26,300	1950	500	Fractured crank axles

Transmission	*Driving wheel diameter (in)*	*Tractive effort (lb)*	*Withdrawn*	*Mileage*	*Notes*
EE Co electric	42	41,400	1962	800,000	
EE Co electric	42	41,400	1966	1,100,000	Longest running diesel prototype
BTH electric		34,500	1960	100,000	Rebuilt as *Hawk* by Brush
Fell mechanical	51	28,000	1962	80,000	Boiler fire
EE Co electric	43	48,000	1962	700,000	Regeared to 90 mph
EE Co electric	43	48,000	1962	600,000	Regeared to 90 mph
EE Co electric	43	50,000	1962	480,000	Similar to Class 40
EE Co electric	43	55,000	1961	450,000	In Science Museum
EE Co electric	48	33,000	1965	32,000	On Worth Valley Railway
Krupp Mechanical	48	33,000	1957	–	
Brush electric	43	70,000	1975	550,000	
AEI electric	45	55,000	1964	80,000	BRCW in liquidation
EE Co electric	42	50,000	1967	627,000	In accident at Thirsk
Brush electric	45	51,000	1967	300,000	Re-engined by EE Co
Brush electric	43	70,000	1971	125,000	Sold to USSR
Brush electric	45	55,000	1978		Converted to 47 901
Brush electric	45	55,000			In service in Western Region

Electric locomotives

Locomotive number	*Built*	*Builder*	*Brake horse-power*	*Wheel arrange-ment*	*Weight (tons)*	*Axle load (tons)*	*Max speed (mph)*	*Voltage (dc)*
CC1	1941	SR	1,470	Co-Co	99.7	16.6	75	750

Gas turbine locomotives

Locomotive number	*Built*	*Builder*	*Brake horse-power*	*Wheel arrange-ment*	*Weight (tons)*	*Axle load (tons)*	*Max speed (mph)*	*Gas Turbine*
18000	1950	Brown Boveri	2,500	A1A–A1A	119.1	20.6	90	Brown Boveri
18100	1951	Metropolitan Vickers	3,500	Co-Co	129.5	22.0	90	Metrovick
GT3	1961	English Electric	2,700	4–6–0	123.0	19.8	90	EE Co EM27

Appendix 2

DYNAMOMETER CAR TESTS: OVERALL FUEL CONSUMPTIONS AS TESTED

Steam locomotives

Locomotive	*Steam temp. (°F)*	*Efficiency (%)* max	total	*Watt-hours per ton mile* at rail	fuel input	*Fuel used (lb/ton mile)*
GER No 20	390	4.1				
GWR No 40	398	4.1				
GWR No 40 superheated	498	8.7	6.3	24	409	0.10 coal
Reid-Macleod	700	18.9				
Ljungström						
Sweden			20.8	25.8	123	0.03 coal
Great Britain			7.8	26.5	331	0.08 coal
Kitson-Still						
Steam	320	3.9				
diesel		20.0		25	167	0.03 oil
LNER No 10000	735	14.5	6.3	25.8	410	0.10 coal
LMS No 6399 *Fury*	533		6.2	26	418	0.11 coal
LMS No 6202 Turbomotive	740	18.4	11.2	25.1	228	0.06 coal

No of control steps	*Driving wheel diameter (in)*	*Tractive effort (lb)*	*Withdrawn*	*Mileage*	*Notes*
26	42	40,000	1969	2,200,000	Superseded by Class 71

Transmission	*Driving wheel diameter (in)*	*Tractive effort (lb)*	*Withdrawn*	*Mileage*	*Notes*
Electric	48	30,000	1960	300,000	Converted to UIC test vehicle
Electric	44	55,000	1958	200,000	Converted to 25kV locomotive
Mechanical	69	25,000	1961	17,600	

Diesel locomotives

Locomotive	*Efficiency*		*Watt hours per ton mile*		*Fuel used (lb/ton mile)*
	Max	*tested*	*at rail*	*fuel input*	
Southern Railway No 10203		19.2	24.8	138	0.025 oil
LMR No 10100 Fell		19.0	25.0	132	0.024 oil
English Electric Co *Deltic*		24.0	25.0	105	0.019 oil
English Electric Co DP2		19.7	25.6	130	0.025 oil

Gas turbine locomotives

Locomotive	*Efficiency*		*Watt hours per ton mile*		*Fuel used (lb/ton mile)*
	Max	*tested*	*at rail*	*fuel input*	
Brown Boveri No 18000	19	6.6	25.7	389	0.07 oil

Electric locomotives

Locomotive	*Efficiency*		*Watt hours per ton mile*		*Fuel used (lb/ton mile)*
	Max	*tested*	*at rail*	*fuel input*	
Southern Railway No CC1		12.5	36.8	290	0.07 coal

INDEX